DYSLEXIC EDITION

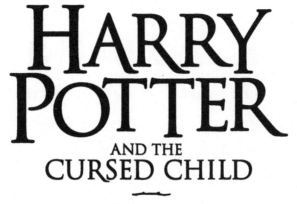

HARRY POTTER

AND THE
CURSED CHILD

PARTS ONE AND TWO

BASED ON AN ORIGINAL NEW STORY BY

J.K. ROWLING

JOHN TIFFANY & JACK THORNE

A NEW PLAY BY **JACK THORNE**

FIRST PRODUCED BY
SONIA FRIEDMAN PRODUCTIONS, COLIN CALLENDER
& HARRY POTTER THEATRICAL PRODUCTIONS

THE OFFICIAL SCRIPT OF THE
ORIGINAL WEST END PRODUCTION

SPECIAL REHEARSAL EDITION

Harry Potter

Potter

AND THE
CURSED CHILD

PARTS ONE AND TWO

W F HOWES LTD

This large print edition published in 2016 by
W F Howes Ltd
Unit 5, St George's House, Rearsby Business Park,
Gaddesby Lane, Rearsby, Leicester LE7 4YH

1 3 5 7 9 10 8 6 4 2

First published in the United Kingdom in 2016
by Little, Brown

A CIP catalogue record for this book is available
from the British Library

ISBN 978 1 51005 131 7

Typeset by Palimpsest Book Production Limited,
Falkirk, Stirlingshire
Printed and bound by
Printforce Nederland b.v., Alphen aan den Rijn
The Netherlands

Contents

**Harry Potter and the Cursed Child
Parts One and Two**
may not be performed in whole or in
part and no use may be made of it
whatsoever except under express licence
from the rights holders of the work,
J.K. Rowling and Harry Potter Theatrical
Productions Limited.

Please email
enquiries@hptheatricalproductions.com
with any enquiries.

J.K. Rowling

**To Jack Thorne
who entered my world
and did beautiful things there.**

John Tiffany

**For Joe, Louis, Max, Sonny and
Merle ... wizards all ...**

Jack Thorne

**To Elliott Thorne, born 7 April 2016.
As we rehearsed, he gurgled.**

Part One

Part One
Act One

Act One
Scene One

King's Cross

A busy and crowded station, full of people trying to go somewhere. Amongst the hustle and bustle, two large cages rattle on top of two laden trolleys. They're being pushed by two boys, James Potter and Albus Potter. Their mother, Ginny, follows after. A thirty-seven-year-old man, Harry, has his daughter Lily on his shoulders.

Albus
> Dad. He keeps saying it.

Harry
> James, give it a rest.

James
I only said he might be in Slytherin. And he might, so . . . **(off his dad's glare)** fine.

Albus (looking up at his mum)
You'll write to me, won't you?

Ginny
Every day if you want us to.

Albus
No. Not every day. James says most people only get letters from home about once a month. I don't want to . . .

Harry
We wrote to your brother three times a week last year.

Albus
What? James!

Albus looks accusingly at James.

Ginny
Yes. You may not want to believe everything he tells you about Hogwarts. He likes a laugh, your brother.

Act One Scene One

James **(with a grin)**
    Can we go now please?

Albus looks at his dad, and then his mum.

Ginny
    All you have to do is walk straight at the wall between platforms nine and ten.

Lily
    I'm so excited.

Harry
    Don't stop and don't be scared you'll crash into it, that's very important. Best to do it at a run if you're nervous.

Albus
    I'm ready.

Harry and Lily put their hands on Albus's trolley – Ginny joins James's trolley – and together, the family run hard into the barrier.

Act One
Scene Two

Platform Nine
and Three-Quarters

**Which is covered in thick
white steam pouring from
the Hogwarts Express.**

**And which is also busy – but
instead of people in sharp suits
going about their day, it's now
wizards and witches in robes
mostly trying to work out how
to say goodbye to their beloved
progeny.**

Albus
  This is it.

Lily
  Wow!

Act One Scene Two

Albus

Platform nine and three-quarters.

Lily

Where are they? Are they here?
Maybe they didn't come?

**Harry points out Ron, Hermione
and their daughter Rose. Lily runs
hard up to them.**

Uncle Ron. Uncle Ron!!!

**Ron turns towards them as Lily
goes barrelling up to him. He picks
her up into his arms.**

Ron

If it isn't my favourite Potter.

Lily

Have you got my trick?

Ron

Are you aware of the Weasleys'
Wizard Wheezes certified nose-stealing
breath?

Rose
	Mum! Dad's doing that lame thing again.

Hermione
	You say lame, he says glorious, I say . . . somewhere in between.

Ron
	Hang on. Let me just munch this . . . air. And now it's just a simple matter of . . . excuse me if I smell slightly of garlic . . .

	He breathes on her face. Lily giggles.

Lily
	You smell of porridge.

Ron
	Bing. Bang. Boing. Young lady, get ready to not being able to smell at all . . .

	He lifts her nose off.

Lily
	Where's my nose?

Act One Scene Two

Ron

Tada!

His hand is empty. It's a lame trick. Everyone enjoys its lameness.

Lily

You are silly.

Albus

Everyone's staring at us again.

Ron

Because of me! I'm extremely famous. My nose experiments are legendary!

Hermione

They're certainly something.

Harry

Parked all right then?

Ron

I did. Hermione didn't believe I could pass a Muggle driving test, did you? She thought I'd have to Confund the examiner.

Part One

Hermione
I thought nothing of the kind, I have complete faith in you.

Rose
And I have complete faith he did Confund the examiner.

Ron
Oi!

Albus
Dad . . .

Albus pulls on Harry's robes. Harry looks down.

Do you think – what if I am – what if I'm put in Slytherin . . .

Harry
And what would be wrong with that?

Albus
Slytherin is the house of the snake, of Dark Magic . . . it's not a house of brave wizards.

Act One Scene Two

Harry
　　Albus Severus, you were named after two headmasters of Hogwarts. One of them was a Slytherin and he was probably the bravest man I ever knew.

Albus
　　But just say . . .

Harry
　　If it matters to you, **you**, the Sorting Hat will take your feelings into account.

Albus
　　Really?

Harry
　　It did for me.

This is something he's never said before, it resonates around his head a moment.

　　Hogwarts will be the making of you, Albus. I promise you, there is nothing to be frightened of there.

James
Apart from the Thestrals. Watch out for the Thestrals.

Albus
I thought they were invisible!

Harry
Listen to your professors, **don't** listen to James, and remember to enjoy yourself. Now, if you don't want this train to leave without you, you should leap on . . .

Lily
I'm going to chase the train out.

Ginny
Lily, come straight back.

Hermione
Rose. Remember to send Neville our love.

Rose
Mum, I can't send a professor love!

Rose exits for the train. And then Albus turns and hugs Ginny and

Harry one last time before following after her.

Albus
  Okay, then. Bye.

He climbs on board. Hermione, Ginny, Ron and Harry stand watching the train – as whistles blow up and down the platform.

Ginny
  They're going to be okay, right?

Hermione
  Hogwarts is a big place.

Ron
  Big. Wonderful. Full of food. I'd give anything to be going back.

Harry
  Strange, Al being worried he'll be sorted into Slytherin.

Hermione
  That's nothing, Rose is worried whether she'll break the Quidditch scoring record in her first or second

year. And how early she can take her
O.W.Ls.

Ron
   I have no idea where she gets her
ambition from.

Ginny
   And how would you feel Harry, if
Al – if he is?

Ron
   You know Gin, we always thought
there was a chance you could be sorted
into Slytherin.

Ginny
   What?

Ron
   Honestly, Fred and George ran a
book.

Hermione
   Can we go? People are looking, you
know.

Ginny
   People always look when you three

are together. And apart. People always look at you.

The four exit. Ginny stops Harry.

Harry . . . he'll be all right, won't he?

Harry
Of course he will.

———

Act One
Scene Three

The Hogwarts Express

**Albus and Rose walk along
the carriage of the train.**

**The Trolley Witch approaches,
pushing her trolley.**

Trolley Witch
    Anything from the trolley, dears?
Pumpkin Pasty? Chocolate Frog?
Cauldron Cake?

**Rose (spotting Albus's loving look
at the Chocolate Frogs)**

    Al. We need to concentrate.

Act One Scene Three

Albus
Concentrate on what?

Rose
On who we choose to be friends with. My mum and dad met your dad on their first Hogwarts Express you know . . .

Albus
So we need to choose now who to be friends with for life? That's quite scary.

Rose
On the contrary, it's exciting. I'm a Granger-Weasley, you're a Potter – everyone will want to be friends with us, we've got the pick of anyone we want.

Albus
So how do we decide – which compartment to go in . . .

Rose
We rate them all and then we make a decision.

Albus opens a compartment door – to look in on a lonely blond kid – Scorpius – in an otherwise empty compartment. Albus smiles. Scorpius smiles back.

Albus
   Hi. Is this compartment . . .

Scorpius
   It's free. It's just me.

Albus
   Great. So we might just – come in – for a bit – if that's okay?

Scorpius
   That's okay. Hi.

Albus
   Albus. Al. I'm – my name is Albus . . .

Scorpius
   Hi Scorpius. I mean, I'm Scorpius. You're Albus. I'm Scorpius. And you must be . . .

Rose's face is growing colder by the minute.

Rose
   Rose.

Scorpius
   Hi Rose. Would you like some of my Fizzing Whizzbees?

Rose
   I've just had breakfast, thanks.

Scorpius
   I've also got some Shock-o-Choc, Pepper Imps and some Jelly Slugs. Mum's idea – she says **(sings),** 'Sweets they always help you make friends' **(he realises that singing was a mistake).** Stupid idea probably.

Albus
   I'll have some . . . Mum doesn't let me have sweets. Which one would you start with?

   Rose hits Albus, out of sight of Scorpius.

Scorpius
   Easy. I've always regarded the Pepper Imp as the king of the confectionery

bag. They're peppermint sweets that make you smoke at the ears.

Albus
Brilliant, then that's what I'll—
(Rose hits him again.) Rose, will you please stop hitting me?

Rose
I'm not hitting you.

Albus
You are hitting me, and it hurts.

Scorpius's face falls.

Scorpius
She's hitting you because of me.

Albus
What?

Scorpius
Listen, I know who you are, so it's probably only fair you know who I am.

Albus
What do you mean you know who I am?

Act One Scene Three

Scorpius
You're Albus Potter. She's Rose Granger-Weasley. And I am Scorpius Malfoy. My parents are Astoria and Draco Malfoy. Our parents – they didn't get on.

Rose
That's putting it mildly. Your mum and dad are Death Eaters!

Scorpius **(affronted)**
Dad was – but Mum wasn't.

Rose looks away, and Scorpius knows why she does.

I know what the rumour is, and it's a lie.

Albus looks from an uncomfortable Rose to a desperate Scorpius.

Albus
What – is the rumour?

Scorpius
The **rumour** is that my parents couldn't have children. That my father

and my grandfather were so desperate
for a powerful heir, to prevent the end
of the Malfoy line, that they . . . that
they used a Time-Turner to send my
mother back—

Albus
 To send her back where?

Rose
 The rumour is that he's Voldemort's
son, Albus.

A horrible, uncomfortable silence.

It's probably rubbish. I mean . . .
look, you've got a nose.

**The tension is slightly broken,
Scorpius laughs, pathetically
grateful.**

Scorpius
 And it's just like my father's! I got
his nose, his hair and his name. Not
that that's a great thing either. I mean –
father-son issues, I have them. But, on
the whole, I'd rather be a Malfoy than,
you know, the son of the Dark Lord.

Act One Scene Three

Scorpius and Albus look at each other and something passes between them.

Rose
Yes, well, we probably should sit somewhere else. Come on, Albus.

Albus is thinking deeply.

Albus
No **(off Rose's look)**, I'm okay. You go on . . .

Rose
Albus. I won't wait.

Albus
And I wouldn't expect you to. But I'm staying here.

Rose looks at him a second and then leaves the compartment.

Rose
Fine!

Scorpius and Albus are left – looking at each other – unsure.

Scorpius
    Thank you.

Albus
    No. No. I didn't stay – for you – I
stayed for your sweets.

Scorpius
    She's quite fierce.

Albus
    Yes. Sorry.

Scorpius
    No. I like it. Do you prefer Albus or Al?

**Scorpius grins and pops two
sweets in his mouth.**

Albus **(thinks)**
    Albus.

Scorpius **(as smoke comes out of
his ears)**
    Thank you for staying for
my sweets, Albus!

Albus **(laughing)**
    Wow.

Act One
Scene Four

Transition Scene

And now we enter a never-world of time change. And this scene is all about magic.

The changes are rapid as we leap between worlds. There are no individual scenes, but fragments, shards that show the constant progression of time.

Initially we're inside Hogwarts, in the Great Hall, and everyone is dancing around Albus.

Polly Chapman
Albus Potter.

Part One

Karl Jenkins
  A Potter. In our year.

Yann Fredericks
  He's got his hair. He's got hair just like him.

Rose
  And he's my cousin. **(As they turn.)** Rose Granger-Weasley. Nice to meet you.

  The Sorting Hat walks through the students who spring into their houses.

  It becomes quickly apparent he's approaching Rose, who is tense as she awaits her fate.

Sorting Hat
  I've done this job for centuries

  On every student's head I've sat

  Of thoughts I take inventories

  For I'm the famous Sorting Hat.

  I've sorted high, I've sorted low,

  I've done the job through thick and thin

So put me on and you will know
Which house you should be in . . .
Rose Granger-Weasley.

He puts his hat on Rose's head.

GRYFFINDOR!

There's cheering from the Gryffindors as Rose joins them.

Rose
Thank Dumbledore.

Scorpius runs to take Rose's place under the Sorting Hat's glare.

Sorting Hat
Scorpius Malfoy.

He puts his hat on Scorpius's head.

Slytherin!

Scorpius was expecting this, he nods and half smiles. There's cheering from the Slytherins as he joins them.

Polly Chapman
    Well, that makes sense.

Albus walks swiftly to the front of the stage.

Sorting Hat
    Albus Potter.

He puts his hat on Albus's head – and this time he seems to take longer – almost like he too is confused.

    Slytherin!

There's a silence.

A perfect, profound silence.

One that sits low, twists a bit and has damage within it.

Polly Chapman
    Slytherin?

Craig Bowker Jr
    Whoah! A Potter? In Slytherin.

Albus looks out, unsure.

Act One   Scene Four

Scorpius smiles, delighted, as he shouts across to him.

Scorpius
   You can stand next to me!

Albus **(thoroughly discombobulated)**
   Right. Yes.

Yann Fredericks
   I suppose his hair isn't that similar.

Rose
   Albus? But this is wrong, Albus. This is not how it's supposed to be.

And suddenly a flying lesson is happening with Madam Hooch.

Madam Hooch
   Well, what are you all waiting for? Everyone stand by a broomstick. Come on, hurry up.

The kids all hurry into position beside their brooms.

   Stick out your hands out over your broom, and say, 'Up!'

Everyone
Up!

Rose's and Yann's brooms sail into their hands.

Rose **and** Yann
Yes!

Madam Hooch
Come on now, I've no time for shirkers. Say 'up'. 'Up' like you mean it.

Everyone **(bar Rose and Yann)**
Up!

Brooms sail up, including Scorpius's. Only Albus is left with his broom on the floor.

Everyone **(bar Rose, Yann and Albus)**
Yes!

Albus
Up. UP. UP.

His broom doesn't move. Not even a millimetre. He stares at it with

disbelieving desperation. There's giggling from the rest of the class.

Polly Chapman
Oh Merlin's beard, how humiliating! He really isn't like his father at all is he?

Karl Jenkins
Albus Potter, the Slytherin Squib.

Madam Hooch
Okay. Children. Time to fly.

And suddenly Harry appears from nowhere beside Albus as steam expands all over the stage. We're back on platform nine and three-quarters and time has ticked on mercilessly. Albus is now a year older (as is Harry, but less noticeably).

Albus
I'm just asking you Dad if you'll – if you'll just stand a little away from me.

Harry **(amused)**
Second-years don't like to be seen with their dads is that it?

**An Over-Attentive Wizard
begins to circle them.**

Albus
   No. It's just – you're **you** and – and
I'm me and—

Harry
   It's just people looking okay? People
look. And they're looking at me, not
you.

**The Over-Attentive Wizard
proffers something for Harry to sign
– he signs it.**

Albus
   At Harry Potter and his disappointing
son.

Harry
   What does that mean?

Albus
   At Harry Potter and his Slytherin son.

**James rushes past them carrying
his bag.**

Act One Scene Four

James

Slythering Slytherin, stop with your dithering, time to get on to the train.

Harry

Unnecessary, James.

James **(long gone)**

See you at Christmas, Dad.

Harry looks at Albus, concerned.

Harry

Al—

Albus

My name is Albus, not Al.

Harry

Are the other kids being unkind? Is that it? Maybe if you tried making a few more friends – without Hermione and Ron I wouldn't have survived Hogwarts, I wouldn't have survived at all.

Albus

But I don't need a Ron and Hermione – I've – I've got a friend, Scorpius, and I know you don't like him but he's all I need.

Harry
 Look, as long as you're happy, that's all that matters to me.

Albus
 You didn't need to bring me to the station, Dad.

Albus picks up his case and makes hard away.

Harry
 But I **wanted** to be here . . .

But Albus is gone. Draco Malfoy, his robes perfect, his blond ponytail precisely placed, emerges from within the crowds to be beside Harry.

Draco
 I need a favour.

Harry
 Draco.

Draco
 These rumours – about my son's parentage – they don't seem to be going

away. The other Hogwarts students tease Scorpius about it relentlessly – if the Ministry could release a statement re-affirming that all Time-Turners were destroyed in the Battle of the Department of Mysteries . . .

Harry
    Draco, just let it blow over – they'll soon move on.

Draco
    My son is suffering and – Astoria hasn't been well recently – so he needs all the support he can get.

Harry
    If you answer the gossip, you feed the gossip. There've been rumours Voldemort had a child for years, Scorpius is not the first to be accused. The Ministry, for your sake as well as ours, needs to steer well clear.

Draco frowns, annoyed, as the stage clears and Rose and Albus stand ready with their cases.

Albus
　As soon as the train leaves you don't have to talk to me.

Rose
　I know. We just need to keep the pretence up in front of the grown-ups.

　Scorpius runs on – with big hopes and an even bigger case.

Scorpius **(hopeful)**
　Hi Rose.

Rose **(definitive)**
　Bye Albus.

Scorpius **(still hopeful)**
　She's melting.

　And suddenly we're in the Great Hall and Professor McGonagall is standing at the front, with a big smile on her face.

Professor McGonagall
　And I'm pleased to announce Gryffindor's newest member of the Quidditch team – our – **(she realises**

she can't be partial) your superb new Chaser – Rose Granger-Weasley.

The Hall erupts into cheers. Scorpius claps alongside them all.

Albus
Are you clapping her too? We hate Quidditch and she's playing for another house.

Scorpius
She's your cousin, Albus.

Albus
Do you think she'd clap for me?

Scorpius
I think she's brilliant.

The students circle Albus again as suddenly a Potions class begins.

Polly Chapman
Albus Potter. An irrelevance. Even portraits turn the other way when he comes up the stairs.

Albus hunches over a potion.

39

Part One

Albus
   And now we add – is it horn of
Bicorn?

Karl Jenkins
   Leave him and Voldemort's child to it,
I say.

Albus
   With just a little salamander
blood . . .

The potion explodes loudly.

Scorpius
   Okay. What's the counter-ingredient?
What do we need to change?

Albus
   Everything.

**And with that, time moves ever
onwards – Albus's eyes become
darker, his face grows more sallow.
He's still an attractive boy, but he's
trying not to admit it.**

**And suddenly he's back on platform
nine and three-quarters with his dad**

– who is still trying to persuade his son (and himself) that everything is okay. Both have aged another year.

Harry
    Third year. Big year. Here is your permission form for Hogsmeade.

Albus
    I hate Hogsmeade.

Harry
    How can you hate a place you haven't actually visited yet?

Albus
    Because I know it'll be full of Hogwarts students.

Albus screws up the paper.

Harry
    Just give it a go – come on – this is your chance to go nuts in Honeydukes without your mum knowing – no Albus, don't you dare.

Albus **(pointing his wand)**
    Incendio!

The ball of paper bursts into flame, and ascends across the stage.

Harry
Of all the stupid things!

Albus
The ironic thing is I didn't expect it to work. I'm terrible at that spell.

Harry
Al–Albus, I've been exchanging owls with Professor McGonagall – she says you're isolating yourself – you're uncooperative in lessons – you're surly – you're—

Albus
So what would you like me to do? Magic myself popular? Conjure myself into a new house? Transfigure myself into a better student? Just cast a spell, Dad, and change me into what you want me to be, okay? It'll work better for both of us. Got to go. Train to catch. Friend to find.

Albus runs to Scorpius, who is sitting on his case – numb to the world.

Act One   Scene Four

(delighted) Scorpius . . .

(concerned) Scorpius . . . are you okay?

Scorpius says nothing. Albus tries to read his friend's eyes.

Your mum? It's got worse?

Scorpius
It's got the worst it can possibly get.

Albus sits down beside Scorpius.

Albus
I thought you'd send an owl . . .

Scorpius
I couldn't work out what to say.

Albus
And now I don't know what to say . . .

Scorpius
Say nothing.

Albus
Is there anything . . .

Scorpius
> Come to the funeral.

Albus
> Of course.

Scorpius
> And be my good friend.

And suddenly the Sorting Hat is centre stage and we're back in the Great Hall.

Sorting Hat
> Are you afraid of what you'll hear?
>
> Afraid I'll speak the name you fear?
>
> Not Slytherin! Not Gryffindor!
>
> Not Hufflepuff! Not Ravenclaw!
>
> Don't worry, child, I know my job,
>
> You'll learn to laugh, if first you sob.
>
> Lily Potter. Gryffindor!

Lily
> Yes!

Albus
> Great.

Act One Scene Four

Scorpius
  Did you really think she'd come to us? Potters don't belong in Slytherin.

Albus
  This one does.

  As he tries to melt into the background, the other students laugh. He looks up at them all.

  I didn't choose, you know that? I didn't choose to be his son.

———

Act One
Scene Five

Ministry of Magic, Harry's Office

Hermione sits with piles of paper in front of her in Harry's messy office. She is slowly sorting through it all. Harry enters in a rush. He is bleeding from a graze on his cheek.

Hermione
> How did it go?

Harry
> It was true.

Hermione
> Theodore Nott?

Harry
> In custody.

Act One   Scene Five

Hermione
And the Time-Turner itself?

Harry reveals the Time-Turner. It shines out alluringly.

Is it genuine? Does it work? It's not just an Hour-Reversal Turner – it goes back further?

Harry
We don't know anything yet. I wanted to try it out there and then but wiser heads prevailed.

Hermione
Well, now we have it.

Harry
And you're sure you want to keep it?

Hermione
I don't think we've a choice. Look at it. It's entirely different to the Time-Turner I had.

Harry **(dryly)**
Apparently wizardry has moved on since we were kids.

Hermione
You're bleeding.

Harry checks his face in the mirror. He dabs at the wound with his robes.

Don't worry, it'll go with the scar.

Harry **(with a grin)**
What you doing in my office, Hermione?

Hermione
I was anxious to hear about Theodore Nott and – thought I'd check whether you'd kept your promise and were on top of your paperwork.

Harry
Ah. Turns out I'm not.

Hermione
No. You're not. Harry, how can you get any work done in this chaos?

Harry waves his wand and the papers and books transform into neat piles. Harry smiles.

Act One   Scene Five

Harry
    No longer chaotic.

Hermione
    But still ignored. You know there's some interesting stuff in here . . . there are mountain trolls riding graphorns through Hungary, there are giants with winged tattoos on their backs walking through the Greek Seas, and the werewolves have gone entirely underground—

Harry
    Great, let's get out there. I'll get the team together.

Hermione
    Harry, I get it. Paperwork's boring . . .

Harry
    Not for you.

Hermione
    I'm busy enough with my own. These are people and beasts that fought along-side Voldemort in the great wizarding wars. These are allies of darkness. This

– combined with what we have just unearthed at Theodore Nott's – could mean something. But if the Head of Magical Law Enforcement isn't reading his files—

Harry
    But I don't need to read it – I'm out there, hearing about it. Theodore Nott – it was me who heard the rumours about the Time-Turner and me who acted upon it. You really don't need to tell me off.

Hermione looks at Harry – this is tricky.

Hermione
    Do you fancy a toffee? Don't tell Ron.

Harry
    You're changing the subject.

Hermione
    I truly am. Toffee?

Harry
    Can't. We're off sugar at the moment.

Beat.

You know, you can get addicted to that stuff?

Hermione
What can I say? My parents were dentists, I was bound to rebel at some point. Forty is leaving it a little late, but . . . you've just done a brilliant thing. You're certainly not being told off – I just need you to look at your paper-work every now and again, that's all. Consider this a gentle – nudge – from the **Minister for Magic**.

Harry hears the implication in her emphasis; he nods.

How's Ginny? How's Albus?

Harry
It seems I'm as good at fatherhood as I am at paperwork. How's Rose? How's Hugo?

Hermione **(with a grin)**
You know, Ron says he thinks I see more of my secretary Ethel (**she**

51

indicates off) than him. Do you think there's a point where we made a choice – parent of the year or – Ministry official of the year? Go on. Go home to your family Harry, the Hogwarts Express is about to depart for another year – enjoy the time you've got left – and then come back here with a fresh head and get these files read.

Harry
   You really think this could all mean something?

Hermione **(with a smile)**
   It could do. But if it does, we'll find a way to fight it, Harry. We always have.

She smiles once more – pops a toffee in her mouth and leaves the office. Harry is left alone. He packs his bag. He walks out of the office and down a corridor. The weight of the world upon his shoulders.

He walks, tired, into a telephone box. He dials 62442.

Act One Scene Five

Telephone Box
Farewell, Harry Potter.

He ascends away from the Ministry of Magic.

Act One
Scene Six

Harry and Ginny Potter's House

Albus can't sleep. He is sitting at the top of the stairs. He hears voices below him. We hear Harry's voice before he's revealed. An elderly man in a wheelchair is with him, Amos Diggory.

Harry
   Amos, I understand, I really do – but I'm only just home and—

Amos
   I've tried to make appointments at the Ministry. They say 'Ah, Mr Diggory, we have an appointment for you, let's see, in two months.' I wait. Very patiently.

Act One   Scene Six

Harry
—and coming to my house in the middle of the night – when my kids are just getting ready for their new year at school – it's not right.

Amos
Two months pass, I receive an owl, 'Mr Diggory, I'm awfully sorry, but Mr Potter has been called away on urgent business, we're going to have to shift things around a little, are you available for an appointment in, let's see, two months' time.' And then it repeats again, and again . . . You're shutting me out.

Harry
Of course I'm not. It's just, I'm afraid, as Head of the Department of Magical Law Enforcement I'm responsible—

Amos
There's plenty you're responsible for.

Harry
Sorry?

Amos

My son, Cedric, you do remember Cedric, don't you?

Harry **(remembering Cedric hurts him)**

Yes, I remember your son. His loss—

Amos

Voldemort wanted **you**! Not my son! You told me yourself, the words he said were 'kill the spare'. The spare. My son, my beautiful son, was a spare.

Harry

Mr Diggory, as you know, I sympathise with your efforts to memorialise Cedric but—

Amos

A memorial? I am not interested in a memorial – not any more. I am an old man – an old, dying man – and I am here to ask you – beg you – to help me get him back.

Harry looks up, astonished.

Act One   Scene Six

Harry
  Get him back? Amos, that's not
possible.

Amos
  The Ministry has a Time-Turner does
it not?

Harry
  The Time-Turners were all destroyed.

Amos
  The reason I'm here with such
urgency is I've just heard rumour –
strong rumour – that the Ministry seized
an illegal Time-Turner from Theodore
Nott and has kept it. For investigation.
Let me use that Time-Turner. Let me
have my son back.

**There's a long, deadly pause.
Harry is finding this extremely
difficult. We watch as Albus moves
closer, listening.**

Harry
  Amos, playing with time? You know
we can't do that.

Amos
How many people have died for the Boy Who Lived? I'm asking you to save one of them.

This hurts Harry. He thinks, his face hardens.

Harry
Whatever you've heard – the Theodore Nott story is a fiction, Amos. I'm sorry.

Delphi
Hello.

Albus jumps a mile as Delphi – a twenty-something determined-looking woman – is revealed looking through the stairs at him.

Oh. Sorry. Didn't mean to startle. I used to be a big stair-listener myself. Sitting there. Waiting for someone to say something the tiniest bit interesting.

Albus
Who are you? Because this is sort of my house and . . .

Act One Scene Six

Delphi
I'm a thief of course. I'm about to steal everything you own. Give me your gold, your wand and your Chocolate Frogs! **(She looks fierce and then smiles.)** Either that or I'm Delphini Diggory. **(She ascends the stairs and sticks out a hand.)** Delphi. I look after him – Amos – well, I try. **(She indicates Amos.)** And you are?

Albus **(rueful grin)**
Albus.

Delphi
Of course! Albus Potter! So Harry is your dad? That's a bit wow isn't it?

Albus
Not really.

Delphi
Ah. Have I just put my foot in it? It's what they used to say about me at school. Delphini Diggory – there isn't a hole she couldn't dig herself into.

Albus
They do all sorts with my name too.

Pause. She looks at him carefully.

Amos
Delphi.

She makes to depart and then hesitates. She smiles at Albus.

Delphi
We don't choose who we're related to. Amos isn't just my patient, he's my uncle, it's part of the reason I took the job at Upper Flagley. But that's made it difficult. It's tough to live with people stuck in the past, isn't it?

Amos
Delphi!

Albus
Upper Flagley?

Delphi
St Oswald's Home for Old Witches and Wizards. Come see us some time. If you like.

Amos
Delphi!

She smiles and then trips as she travels down the stairs. She enters the room with Amos and Harry in it. Albus watches her.

Delphi
  Yes, Uncle?

Amos
  Meet the once-great Harry Potter, now a stone-cold Ministry man. I will leave you in peace, sir. If peace is the right word for it. Delphi, my chair . . .

Delphi
  Yes, Uncle.

Amos is pushed out of the room. Harry is left, looking forlorn. Albus watches on, thinking, carefully.

Act One
Scene Seven

Harry and Ginny Potter's House, Albus's Room

Albus is sitting on the bed as the world goes on outside his door. Still against the constant motion outside. We hear a roar from James (from off).

Ginny
    James, please, ignore your hair, and tidy that damn room . . .

James
    How can I ignore it? It's pink! I'm going to have to use my Invisibility Cloak!

Act One Scene Seven

James appears at the door, he has pink hair.

Ginny
That's **not** why your dad gave you that cloak!

Lily
Who's seen my Potions book?

Ginny
Lily Potter, don't think you're wearing those to school tomorrow . . .

Lily appears at Albus's door. She's wearing fairy wings that flutter.

Lily
I love them. They're fluttery.

She exits as Harry appears in Albus's doorway. He looks through.

Harry
Hi.

There's an awkward pause between them. Ginny appears in the

doorway. She sees what's happening and stays a moment.

Just delivering a pre-Hogwarts gift – gifts – Ron's sent this . . .

Albus
  Okay, a love potion. Okay.

Harry
  I think it's a joke about – I don't know what. Lily got farting gnomes, James got a comb that's made his hair turn a shade of pink. Ron – well, Ron's Ron you know?

Harry puts down Albus's love potion on his bed.

I also – this is from me . . .

He reveals a small blanket. Ginny looks at it – she sees Harry is trying, and then she softly walks away.

Albus
  An old blanket?

Act One Scene Seven

Harry

I thought a lot about what to give you this year. James – well, James has been going on about the Invisibility Cloak since time itself, and Lily – I knew she'd love wings – but you. You're fourteen years old now, Albus, and I wanted to give you something which – meant something. This – is the last thing I had from my mum. The only thing. I was given to the Dursleys wrapped in it. I thought it had gone forever and then – when your Great Aunt Petunia died, hidden amongst her possessions, surprisingly, Dudley found this – and he kindly sent it on to me, and ever since then – well, any time I've wanted luck I've found it and just tried to hold it and I wondered if you . . .

Albus

Wanted to hold it too? Okay. Done. Let's hope it brings me luck. I certainly need some.

He touches the blanket.

But you should keep it.

Harry

I think – believe – Petunia wanted me to have it, that's why she kept it and now I want you to have it from me. I didn't really know my mother – but I think she'd have wanted you to have it too. And maybe I could come find you – and it – on Hallows' Eve. I'd like to be with it on the night they died – and that could be good for the two of us . . .

Albus

Listen, I've got quite a lot of packing to do, and you undoubtedly have Ministry work coming out of your ears so . . .

Harry

Albus, I want you to have the blanket.

Albus

And do what with it? Fairy wings make sense, Dad, Invisibility Cloaks, they also make sense – but this – really?

Harry is slightly heartbroken. He looks at his son, desperate to reach out.

Act One Scene Seven

Harry

Do you want a hand? Packing. I always loved packing. It meant I was leaving Privet Drive and going back to Hogwarts. Which was . . . well, I know you don't love it but . . .

Albus

For you, it's the greatest place on earth. I know. The poor orphan, bullied by his Uncle and Aunt Dursley—

Harry

Albus, please – can we just—

Albus

—traumatised by his cousin Dudley, saved by Hogwarts. I know it all, Dad. Blah blah blah.

Harry

I'm not going to rise to your bait, Albus Potter.

Albus

The poor orphan who went on to save us all – so may I say – on behalf of wizarding kind. How grateful we are for your heroism. Should we bow now or will a curtsey do?

Harry
    Albus, please – you know, I've never wanted gratitude.

Albus
    But right now I'm overflowing with it – it must be the kind gift of this mouldy blanket that did it . . .

Harry
    Mouldy blanket?

Albus
    What did you think would happen? We'd hug. I'd tell you I always loved you. What? What?

Harry **(finally losing his temper)**
    You know what? I'm done with being made responsible for your unhappiness. At least you've got a dad. Because I didn't, okay?

Albus
    And you think that was unlucky? I don't.

68

Harry
    You wish me dead?

Albus
    No! I just wish you weren't my dad.

Harry **(seeing red)**
    Well, there are times I wish you weren't my son.

There's a silence. Albus nods. Pause. Harry realises what he's said.

    No, I didn't mean that . . .

Albus
    Yes. You did.

Harry
    Albus, you just know how to get under my skin . . .

Albus
    You meant it, Dad. And, honestly, I don't blame you.

There's a horrible pause.

You should probably leave me alone now.

Harry
    Albus, please . . .

Albus picks up the blanket and throws it. It collides with Ron's love potion, which spills all over the blanket and the bed, producing a small puff of smoke.

Albus
    No luck or love for me, then.

Albus runs out of the room. Harry goes after him.

Harry
    Albus. Albus . . . please . . .

Act One
Scene Eight

Dream, Hut-on-the-Rock

**There's a large boom. Then
there's a large crash. Dudley
Dursley, Aunt Petunia and
Uncle Vernon are cowering
behind a bed.**

Dudley Dursley
Mum, I don't like this.

Aunt Petunia
I knew we made a mistake coming
here. Vernon. Vernon. There's nowhere
we can hide. Not even a lighthouse is
far enough away!

There's another large boom.

71

Uncle Vernon
   Hold on. Hold on. Whatever it is, it's not coming in here.

Aunt Petunia
   We're cursed! He's cursed us! The boy has cursed us! **(Seeing Young Harry.)** This is all your fault. Get back in your hole.

Young Harry flinches as Uncle Vernon holds out his rifle.

Uncle Vernon
   Whoever's there I should warn you – I'm armed.

There's a massive smash. And the door falls off its hinges. Hagrid stands in the middle of the door. He looks at them all.

Hagrid
   Couldn't make us a cup o' tea, could yeh? It's not been an easy journey.

Dudley Dursley
   Look. At. Him.

Act One   Scene Eight

Uncle Vernon

Stand back. Stand back. Behind me, Petunia. Behind me, Dudley. I'll soon see this scarramanger off.

Hagrid

Scarrawhat? **(He picks up Uncle Vernon's gun.)** Haven't seen one of these for a while. (**He twists the end of the gun and ties it in a knot.**) Oops-a-daisy. (**And then he gets distracted. He's seen Young Harry.**) Harry Potter.

Young Harry

Hello.

Hagrid

Las' time I saw yeh, yeh was only a baby. Yeh look a lot like yer dad, but yeh've got yer mum's eyes.

Young Harry

You knew my parents?

Hagrid

Where's me manners? A very happy birthday to yeh. Got summat fer yeh here – I mighta sat on it at some point, but it'll taste all right.

From inside his coat he pulls a slightly squashed chocolate cake with 'Happy Birthday Harry' written on it in green icing.

Young Harry
Who are you?

Hagrid **(laughing)**
True, I haven't introduced meself. Rubeus Hagrid, Keeper of Keys and Grounds at Hogwarts. **(He looks around himself.)** What about that tea then, eh? I'd not say no ter summat stronger if yeh've got it, mind.

Young Harry
Hogwhere?

Hagrid
Hogwarts. Yeh'll know all about Hogwarts, o' course.

Young Harry
Er – no. Sorry.

Hagrid
Sorry? It's them as should be sorry! I

knew yeh weren't gettin' yer letters but I never thought yeh wouldn't even know abou' Hogwarts, fer cryin' out loud! Did yeh never wonder where yer parents learnt it all?

Young Harry
   Learnt what?

Hagrid turns menacingly towards Uncle Vernon.

Hagrid
   Do you mean ter tell me, that this boy – this boy! – knows nothin' abou' – about anything?

Uncle Vernon
   I forbid you to tell the boy anything more!

Young Harry
   Tell me what?

Hagrid looks at Uncle Vernon and then at Young Harry.

Hagrid

   Harry – yer a wizard – yeh changed everything. Yer the most famous wizard in the whole world.

And then right from the back of the room and whispering around everyone, words said with an unmistakeable voice. The voice of Voldemort . . .

Haaarry Pottttter . . .

Act One
Scene Nine

Harry and Ginny Potter's House, Bedroom

Harry wakes suddenly. Breathing deeply in the night.

He waits a moment. Calming himself. And then he feels intense pain, in his forehead. In his scar. Around him Dark Magic moves.

Ginny
  Harry . . .

Harry
  It's fine. Go back to sleep.

Ginny
  Lumos.

The room is filled with light from her wand. Harry looks at her.

A nightmare?

Harry
   Yes.

Ginny
   About what?

Harry
   The Dursleys – well it started there –
then it became something else.

**Pause. Ginny looks at him – trying
to work out where he is.**

Ginny
   Do you want a Sleeping Draught?

Harry
   No. I'll be fine. Go back to sleep.

Ginny
   You don't seem fine.

Harry says nothing.

(Seeing his agitation.) It can't have been easy – with Amos Diggory.

Harry
The anger I can cope with, the fact he's right is harder. Amos lost his son because of me—

Ginny
That doesn't seem particularly fair on yourself—

Harry
—and there's nothing I can say – nothing I can say to anyone – unless it's the wrong thing of course.

Ginny knows what – or rather who – he's referring to.

Ginny
So that's what's upsetting you? The night before Hogwarts, it's never a good night if you don't want to go. Giving Al the blanket. It was a nice try.

Harry
It went pretty badly wrong from there. I said some things Ginny . . .

Ginny
    I heard.

Harry
    And you're still talking to me?

Ginny
    Because I know that when the time is right you'll say sorry. That you didn't mean it. That what you said concealed – other things. You can be honest with him Harry . . . that's all he needs.

Harry
    I just wish he was more like James or Lily.

Ginny (dryly)
    Yeah, maybe don't be that honest.

Harry
    No, I wouldn't change a thing about him . . . but I can understand them and . . .

Ginny
    Albus is different and isn't that a good thing. And he can tell – you know –

when you're putting on your Harry Potter front. He wants to see the real you.

Harry
'The truth is a beautiful and terrible thing, and should therefore be treated with great caution.'

Ginny looks at him, surprised.

Dumbledore.

Ginny
A strange thing to say to a child.

Harry
Not when you believe that child will have to die to save the world.

Harry gasps again – and does all he can not to touch his forehead.

Ginny
Harry. What's wrong?

Harry
Fine. I'm fine. I hear you. I'll try to be—

Ginny
> Does your scar hurt?

Harry
> No. No. I'm fine. Now, Nox that and let's get some sleep.

Ginny
> Harry. How long has it been since your scar hurt?

Harry turns to Ginny, his face says it all.

Harry
> Twenty-two years.

Act One
Scene Ten

The Hogwarts Express

**Albus walks quickly
along the train.**

Rose
  Albus, I've been looking for you . . .

Albus
  Me? Why?

**Rose isn't sure how to phrase
what she has to say.**

Rose
  Albus, it's the start of the fourth year,
and so the start of a new year for us. I
want to be friends again.

Albus
　　We never were friends.

Rose
　　That's harsh! You were my best
friend when I was six!

Albus
　　That was a long time ago.

**He makes to walk away, she pulls
him into an empty compartment.**

Rose
　　Have you heard the rumours? Big
Ministry raid a few days ago. Your dad
apparently was incredibly brave.

Albus
　　How do you always know about these
things and I don't?

Rose
　　Apparently he – the wizard they
raided – Theodore Nott I think – had all
sorts of artefacts that broke all sorts of
laws including – and this has got them
all gooey – an illegal Time-Turner. And
quite a superior one at that.

Act One Scene Ten

Albus looks at Rose, everything falling into place.

Albus
    A Time-Turner? My dad found a Time-Turner?

Rose
    Sh! Yes. I know. Great, right?

Albus
    You're sure.

Rose
    Entirely.

Albus
    Now I have to find Scorpius.

He walks down the train. Rose follows, still determined to say her piece.

Rose
    Albus!

Albus turns decisively.

Albus
Who's told you that you have to talk to me?

Rose **(sprung)**
Okay, maybe your mum owled my dad – but only because she's worried about you. And I just think—

Albus
Leave me alone, Rose.

Scorpius is sitting in his usual compartment. Albus enters first, Rose still tailing him.

Scorpius
Albus! Oh hello Rose, what do you smell of?

Rose
What do I **smell** of?

Scorpius
No, I meant it as a nice thing. You smell like a mixture of fresh flowers and fresh – bread.

Act One Scene Ten

Rose
  Albus, I'm here, okay? If you need me.

Scorpius
  I mean, nice bread, good bread, bread . . . what's wrong with bread?

Rose walks away, shaking her head.

Rose
  What's wrong with bread!

Albus
  I've been looking for you everywhere . . .

Scorpius
  And now you've found me. Tada! I was hardly hiding. You know how I like to . . . get on early. Stops people staring. Shouting. Writing 'son of Voldemort' on my trunk. That one never gets old. She really doesn't like me does she?

Albus hugs his friend. With fierceness. They hold for a beat. Scorpius is surprised by this.

Part One

Okay. Hello. Um. Have we hugged before? Do we hug?

The two boys awkwardly dislocate.

Albus
  Just a slightly weird twenty-four hours.

Scorpius
  What's happened in them?

Albus
  I'll explain later. We have to get off this train.

There's the sound of whistles from off. The train starts moving.

Scorpius
  Too late. The train is moving. Hogwarts ahoy!

Albus
  Then we have to get off a moving train.

Trolley Witch
  Anything from the trolley, dears?

Albus opens a window and makes to climb out.

Scorpius
A moving magical train.

Trolley Witch
Pumpkin Pasty? Cauldron Cake?

Scorpius
Albus Severus Potter, get that strange look out of your eye.

Albus
First question. What do you know about the Triwizard Tournament?

Scorpius **(happy)**
Ooooh, a quiz! Three schools pick three champions to compete in three tasks for one Cup. What's that got to do with anything?

Albus
You really are an enormous geek you know that?

Scorpius
Ya-huh.

Part One

Albus
Second question. Why has the Triwizard Tournament not been run in over twenty years?

Scorpius
The last competition included your dad and a boy called Cedric Diggory – they decided to win together but the Cup was a Portkey – and they were transported to Voldemort. Cedric was killed. They cancelled the competition immediately after.

Albus
Good. Third question. Did Cedric need to be killed? Easy question, easy answer: No. The words Voldemort said were 'kill the spare'. The spare. He died only because he was with my father and my father couldn't save him – we can. A mistake has been made and we're going to right it. We're going to use a Time-Turner. We're going to bring him back.

Scorpius
Albus, for obvious reasons, I'm not a massive fan of Time-Turners . . .

Act One Scene Ten

Albus

When Amos Diggory asked for the Time-Turner my father denied they even existed. He lied to an old man who just wanted his son back – who just loved his son. And he did it because he didn't care . . . because he doesn't care. Everyone talks about all the brave things Dad did. But he made some mistakes too. Some big mistakes, in fact. I want to set one of those mistakes right. I want us to save Cedric.

Scorpius

Okay, whatever was holding your brain together seems to have snapped.

Albus

I'm going to do this, Scorpius. I need to do this. And you know as well as I do, I'll entirely mess it up if you don't come with me. Come on.

He grins. And then disappears ever up. Scorpius hesitates for a moment. He makes a face. And then hoists himself up and disappears after Albus.

Act One
Scene Eleven

The Hogwarts Express, Roof

The wind whistles from all angles and it's a fierce wind at that.

Scorpius
Okay, now we're on the roof of a train, it's fast, it's scary, this has been great, I feel like I've learnt a lot about me, something about you, but—

Albus
As I calculate it we should be approaching the viaduct soon and then it'll be a short hike to St Oswald's Home for Old Witches and Wizards . . .

Scorpius
The what? The where? Look, I am as

excited as you are to be a rebel for the
first time in my life – yay – train roof –
fun – but now – oh.

**Scorpius sees something he
doesn't want to see.**

Albus
The water will be an extremely useful
back-up if our Cushioning Charm doesn't
work.

Scorpius
Albus. The Trolley Witch.

Albus
You want a snack for the journey?

Scorpius
No. Albus. The Trolley Witch is
coming towards us.

Albus
No, she can't be, we're on top of the
train . . .

**Scorpius points Albus in the
right direction, and now he can see**

**the Trolley Witch, who approaches
nonchalantly. Pushing her trolley.**

Trolley Witch
  Anything from the trolley, dears?
Pumpkin Pasty? Chocolate Frog?
Cauldron Cake?

Albus
  Oh.

Trolley Witch
  People don't know much about me.
They buy my Cauldron Cakes – but they
never really notice me. I don't
remember the last time someone asked
my name.

Albus
  What is your name?

Trolley Witch
  I've forgotten. All I can tell you is
that when the Hogwarts Express first
came to be – Ottaline Gambol herself
offered me this job . . .

Scorpius
  That's – a hundred and ninety years.

Act One   Scene Eleven

You've been doing this job for a hundred and ninety years?

Trolley Witch
These hands have made over six million Pumpkin Pasties. I've got quite good at them. But what people haven't noticed about my Pumpkin Pasties is how easily they transform into something else . . .

She picks up a Pumpkin Pasty. She throws it like a grenade. It explodes.

And you won't believe what I can do with my Chocolate Frogs. Never. Never. Have I let anyone off this train before they reached their destination. Some have tried – Sirius Black and his cronies, Fred and George Weasley. All have failed. Because this train — it doesn't like people getting off it . . .

The Trolley Witch's hands trans-figure into very sharp spikes. She smiles.

So please retake your seats for the remainder of the journey.

Part One

Albus

    You were right, Scorpius. This train is magical.

Scorpius

    At this precise moment in time, I take no pleasure in being right.

Albus

    But I was also right – about the viaduct – that's water down there, time to try the Cushioning Charm.

Scorpius

    Albus, this is a bad idea.

Albus

    Is it? **(He has a moment's hesitation, then he realises the time for hesitation has passed.)** Too late now. Three. Two. One. Molliare!

He incants as he jumps.

Scorpius

    Albus . . . Albus . . .

He looks down desperately after his friend. He looks at the approaching

Trolley Witch. Her hair wild. Her spikes particularly spiky.

Well, as fun as you clearly look, I have to go after my friend.

He pinches his nose, he jumps after Albus, incanting as he goes.

Molliare!

Act One

Scene Twelve

Ministry of Magic, Grand Meeting Room

The stage is flooded with wizards and witches. They rattle and chatter like all true wizards and witches can. Amongst them, Ginny, Draco and Ron. Above them, on a stage, Hermione and Harry.

Hermione

Order. Order. Do I have to conjure silence? **(She pulls silence from the crowd using her wand.)** Good. Welcome to this Extraordinary General Meeting. I'm so pleased so many of you could make it. The wizarding world has been living in peace now for many years. It's twenty-two years since we defeated Voldemort at the Battle of

Hogwarts and I'm delighted to say there is a new generation being brought up having known only the slightest conflict. Until now. Harry?

Harry
    Voldemort's allies have been showing movement for a few months now. We've followed trolls making their way across Europe, giants starting to cross the seas, and the werewolves – well, I'm distressed to say we lost sight of them some weeks ago. We don't know where they're going or who's encouraged them to move – but we are aware they are moving – and we are concerned what it might mean. So we're asking – if anyone has seen anything? Felt anything? If you could raise a wand, we will hear everyone speak. Professor McGonagall – thank you.

Professor McGonagall
    It did look like the Potions stores had been interfered with when we returned from summer break, but not a huge amount of ingredients were missing, some Boomslang skin and lacewing flies, nothing on the Restricted Register. We put it down to Peeves.

Part One

Hermione
　　Thank you, Professor. We shall investigate. (**She looks around the room.**) Nobody else? Fine, and – gravest of all – and this hasn't been the case since Voldemort – Harry's scar is hurting again.

Draco
　　Voldemort is dead, Voldemort is gone.

Hermione
　　Yes, Draco, Voldemort is dead but these things all lead us to think that there is a possibility that Voldemort – or some trace of Voldemort – might be back.

This gets a reaction.

Harry
　　Now this is difficult but we have to ask it to rule it out. Those of you with a Dark Mark . . . have you felt anything? Even a twinge?

Draco
　　Back to being prejudiced against those with a Dark Mark are we, Potter?

Hermione
    No, Draco. Harry is simply trying to—

Draco
    You know what this is about? Harry just wants his face back in the news-papers again. We've had rumours of Voldemort coming back from the **Daily Prophet** once a year every year—

Harry
    None of those rumours came from me!

Draco
    Really? Doesn't your wife edit the **Daily Prophet**?

Ginny steps towards him, outraged.

Ginny
    The sports pages!

Hermione
    Draco. Harry brought this matter to the attention of the Ministry . . . and I, as Minister for Magic—

Draco
    A vote you only won because you are
his friend.

**Ron is held back by Ginny as he
charges at Draco.**

Ron
    Do you want a smack in the mouth?

Draco
    Face it – his celebrity impacts upon
you all. And how better to get everyone
whispering the Potter name again than
with **(he does an impression of
Harry)** 'my scar is hurting, my scar is
hurting'. And do you know what this all
means – that the gossipmongers once
again have an opportunity to defame my
son with these ridiculous rumours about
his parentage.

Harry
    Draco, no one is saying this has
anything to do with Scorpius . . .

Draco
    Well, I, for one, think this meeting a
sham. And I'm leaving.

He walks out. Others start to disperse after him.

Hermione
No. That's not the way . . . come back. We need a strategy.

———

Act One
Scene Thirteen

St Oswald's Home for Old Witches and Wizards

This is chaos. This is magic. This is St Oswald's Home for Old Witches and Wizards and it is as wonderful as you might hope.

Zimmer frames are conjured into life, knitting wool is enchanted into chaos, and male nurses are made to dance the tango.

These are people relieved of the burden of having to do magic for a reason – instead, these witches and wizards do magic for fun. And what fun they have.

Act One Scene Thirteen

Albus and Scorpius enter, looking around themselves, amused, and – let's face it – slightly scared.

Albus **and** Scorpius
Um, excuse me . . . Excuse me. Excuse me!

Scorpius
Okay, so this place is wild.

Albus
We're looking for Amos Diggory.

There is suddenly total silence. Everything is instantly still. And slightly depressed.

Wool Woman
And what'you boys want with that miserable old sod?

Delphi appears with a smile.

Delphi
Albus? Albus! You came? How wonderful! Come and say hello to Amos!

Act One
Scene Fourteen

St Oswald's Home for Old Witches and Wizards, Amos's Room

Amos looks at Scorpius and Albus, irritated. Delphi watches the three of them.

Amos
So let me get this straight. You over-hear a conversation – a conversation which was not meant for you to overhear – and you decide, without prompting – in fact, without leave – to interfere, and interfere hard, in someone else's business.

Albus
My father lied to you – I know he did – they do have a Time-Turner.

Act One Scene Fourteen

Amos

Of course they do. You can move along now.

Albus

What? No. We're here to help.

Amos

Help? What use could a pair of undersized teenagers be for me?

Albus

My father proved you don't have to be grown up to change the wizarding world.

Amos

So I should allow you to get involved because you're a Potter? Relying on your famous name are you?

Albus

No!

Amos

A Potter who is in Slytherin house – yes, I've read about you – and who brings a Malfoy with him to visit me – a Malfoy who may be a Voldemort? Who's to say you're not involved in Dark Magic?

Albus
But—

Amos
Your information was obvious but the confirmation is useful. Your father did lie. Now leave. The pair of you. And stop wasting my time.

Albus **(with power and strength)**
No, you need to listen to me, you said it yourself – how much blood is on my father's hands. Let me help you change that. Let me help correct one of his mistakes. Trust me.

Amos **(his voice raised)**
Did you not hear me, boy? I see no reason to trust you. So go. Now. Before I **make** you leave.

He raises his wand ominously. Albus looks at the wand – he deflates – Amos has crushed him.

Scorpius
Come on mate, if there's one thing we're good at, it's knowing where we're not wanted.

Act One Scene Fourteen

Albus is reluctant to leave. Scorpius pulls him by the arm. He turns and they walk away.

Delphi
　I can think of one reason why you should trust them, Uncle.

They stop.

　They're the only ones volunteering to help. They're prepared to bravely put themselves at risk to return your son to your side. In fact, I'm pretty sure they put themselves at risk even getting here . . .

Amos
　This is Cedric we're talking about . . .

Delphi
　And – didn't you say yourself – having someone inside Hogwarts might be a **massive** advantage?

Delphi kisses the top of Amos's head. Amos looks at Delphi, and then turns to look at the boys.

Amos
Why? Why do you want to put yourself at risk? What's in it for you?

Albus
I know what it is to be the spare. Your son didn't deserve to be killed, Mr Diggory. We can help you get him back.

Amos **(finally showing emotion)**
My son – my son was the best thing that ever happened to me – and you're right it was an injustice – a gross injustice – if you're serious . . .

Albus
We're deadly serious.

Amos
This is going to be dangerous.

Albus
We know.

Scorpius
Do we?

Amos
    Delphi – perhaps if you were
prepared to accompany them?

Delphi
    If that would make you happy, Uncle.

**She smiles at Albus, he smiles
back.**

Amos
    You do understand even getting the
Time-Turner will risk your lives.

Albus
    We're ready to put our lives at risk.

Scorpius
    Are we?

Amos **(gravely)**
    I hope you have it in you.

Act One
Scene Fifteen

Harry and Ginny Potter's House, Kitchen

**Harry, Ron, Hermione
and Ginny sit eating together.**

Hermione
    I've told Draco again and again – no
one in the Ministry is saying anything
about Scorpius. The rumours aren't
coming from us.

Ginny
    I wrote to him – after he lost Astoria
– to ask if there's anything we could do.
I thought maybe – as he was such a
good friend to Albus – maybe Scorpius
might want to stay over part of the

Christmas break or . . . My owl came back with a letter containing one simple sentence: 'Tell your husband to refute these allegations about my son once and for all.'

Hermione
  He's obsessed.

Ginny
  He's a mess – a grieving mess.

Ron
  And I'm sorry for his loss, but when he accuses Hermione of . . . well . . . **(he looks across at Harry)** Oi droopy drawers, like I say to her all the time, it could be nothing.

Hermione
  Her?

Ron
  The trolls could be going to a party, the giants to a wedding, you could be getting bad dreams because you're worried about Albus, and your scar could be hurting because you're getting old.

Part One

Harry
Getting old? Thanks, mate.

Ron
Honestly, every time I sit down now I make an 'ooof' noise. An 'ooof'. And my feet – the trouble I'm having with my feet – I could write songs about the pain my feet give me – maybe your scar is like that.

Ginny
You talk a lot of rubbish.

Ron
I consider it my speciality. That and my range of Skiving Snackboxes. And my love for all of you. Even Skinny Ginny.

Ginny
If you don't behave, Ronald Weasley, I will tell Mum.

Ron
You wouldn't.

Hermione
If some part of Voldemort survived,

in whatever form, we need to be prepared. And I'm scared.

Ginny
  I'm scared too.

Ron
  Nothing scares me. Apart from Mum.

Hermione
  I mean it, Harry, I will not be Cornelius Fudge on this one. I will not stick my head in the sand. And I don't care how unpopular that makes me with Draco Malfoy.

Ron
  You never really were one for popularity were you?

Hermione shoots Ron a withering look as she aims to hit him but Ron jumps out of the way.

Missed.

Ginny hits Ron. Ron winces.

Hit. A very solid hit.

Part One

Suddenly an owl is in the room. It swoops in low and drops a letter on Harry's plate.

Hermione
   Bit late for an owl isn't it?

Harry opens the letter. Surprised.

Harry
   It's from Professor McGonagall.

Ginny
   What does it say?

Harry's face drops.

Harry
   Ginny, it's Albus – Albus and Scorpius – they never made it to school. They're missing!

———

Act One
Scene Sixteen

Whitehall, Cellar

Scorpius is squinting at a bottle.

Scorpius
So we just take it?

Albus
Scorpius, do I really need to explain to you – uber geek and Potions expert – what Polyjuice does? Thanks to Delphi's brilliant preparation work, we are going to take this potion and be transformed, and thus disguised we will be able to enter the Ministry of Magic.

Scorpius
Okay, two points, one, is it painful?

Delphi
   Very – as I understand it.

Scorpius
   Thank you. Good to know. Second point – do either of you know what Polyjuice tastes of? Because I've heard it tastes of fish, and if it does I will just vomit it back up. Fish doesn't agree with me. Never has. Never will.

Delphi
   Consider us warned. **(She knocks back the potion.)** It doesn't taste of fish. **(She begins to transform. It's agonising.)** Actually it tastes quite pleasant, yum. It is painful but . . . **(She burps, loudly.)** Take it back. There is a – slight – **(She burps again and turns into Hermione.)** Slight – overpowering – fishy residue.

Albus
   Okay, that's – wow!

Scorpius
   Double wow!

Act One Scene Sixteen

Delphi/Hermione
This really doesn't feel how I – I even sound like her! Triple wow!

Albus
Right. Me next.

Scorpius
No. No way, José. If we're doing this, we're doing it **(he puts on a pair of familiar-looking glasses with a smile)** together.

Albus
Three. Two. One.

They swallow.

No, that's good **(he's racked with pain)**. That's less good.

They both start to transform and it's agonising.

Albus turns into Ron, Scorpius into Harry.

The two look at each other. There's a silence.

Albus/Ron
This is going to be slightly weird isn't it?

Scorpius/Harry **(full of drama – he's really enjoying this)**
Go to your room. Go straight to your room. You've been an incredibly awful and bad son.

Albus/Ron **(with a laugh)**
Scorpius . . .

Scorpius/Harry **(tossing his cloak over his shoulder)**
It was your idea – I be him and you be Ron! I just want to have a little fun before I . . . **(And then he burps loudly.)** Okay, so that's utterly horrible.

Albus/Ron
You know, he hides it well, but Uncle Ron's got a bit of a gut growing.

Delphi/Hermione
We should go – don't you think?

Act One Scene Sixteen

They emerge on to the street. They enter a telephone box. They dial 62442.

Telephone Box
    Welcome, Harry Potter.
    Welcome, Hermione Granger.
    Welcome, Ron Weasley.

They smile as the telephone box disappears into the floor.

———

Act One
Scene Seventeen

Ministry of Magic, Meeting Room

Harry, Hermione, Ginny and Draco pace around a small room.

Draco
 Have we searched thoroughly beside the tracks . . .

Harry
 My department have searched once and are searching again.

Draco
 And the Trolley Witch is not able to tell us anything useful?

Hermione
 The Trolley Witch is furious. She

keeps talking about letting down Ottaline Gambol. She prides herself on her Hogwarts delivery record.

Ginny
  Have there been any instances of magic reported by the Muggles?

Hermione
  None so far. I have made the Muggle Prime Minister aware and he is filing what is known as a misper. Sounds like a spell. It isn't.

Draco
  So now we're relying on Muggles to find our children? Have we told them about Harry's scar too?

Hermione
  We're merely asking the Muggles to help. And who knows how Harry's scar might be involved but it's certainly a matter we're taking seriously. Our Aurors are currently investigating anyone involved in Dark Magic and—

Draco
  This is not Death Eater-related.

Hermione
I'm not sure I share your confidence . . .

Draco
I'm not confident, I'm right. The sort of cretins pursuing Dark Magic now. My son is a Malfoy, they wouldn't dare.

Harry
Unless there's something new out there, something to—

Ginny
I agree with Draco – if this is a kidnap – taking Albus I understand, taking them both . . .

Harry locks eyes with Ginny, it becomes clear what she wants him to say.

Draco
And Scorpius is a follower not a leader despite everything I've tried to instil in him. So it's undoubtedly Albus who got him from that train and my question is, where would he take him?

Act One   Scene Seventeen

Ginny
   Harry, they've run away, you and I
know it.

**Draco notices the couple staring at
each other.**

Draco
   Do you? Know it? What aren't you
telling us?

There's a silence.

   Whatever information you're concealing,
I recommend you share it now.

Harry
   Albus and I had an argument, the
day before last.

Draco
   And . . .

**Harry hesitates and then makes
brave eye contact with Draco.**

Harry
   And I told him that there were times
when I wished he weren't my son.

There's another silence. A profoundly powerful one. And then Draco takes a dangerous step towards Harry.

Draco
 If anything happens to Scorpius . . .

Ginny steps in between Draco and Harry.

Ginny
 Don't throw around threats Draco, please don't do that.

Draco **(roar)**
 My son is missing!

Ginny **(an equal roar)**
 So is mine!

He meets her look. There's real emotion in this room.

Draco **(lip curling, every inch his father)**
 If you need gold . . . everything the Malfoys have . . . he's my sole heir . . . he's my – only family.

Hermione
The Ministry has plenty in reserve, thank you Draco.

Draco makes to leave. He stops. He looks at Harry.

Draco
I don't care what you did or who you saved, you are a constant curse on my family, Harry Potter.

Act One
Scene Eighteen

Ministry of Magic, Corridor

Scorpius/Harry
And you're sure it's in there?

A guard walks past. Scorpius/ Harry and Delphi/Hermione try to affect performances.

Yes Minister, I definitely think this is a matter for the Ministry to ponder at length, yes.

Guard **(with a nod)**
Minister.

Delphi/Hermione
Let's ponder it together.

The guard walks on, they let out a sigh of relief.

It was my uncle's idea to use the Veritaserum – we slipped it into a visiting Ministry official's drink. He told us that the Time-Turner had been kept and even told us where – the office of the Minister for Magic herself.

She indicates a door. Suddenly they hear a noise.

Hermione **(from off)**
Harry . . . we should talk about it . . .

Harry **(from off)**
There's nothing to talk about.

Delphi/Hermione
Oh no.

Albus/Ron
Hermione. And Dad.

The panic is instant and infectious.

Scorpius/Harry
Okay. Hiding places. No hiding places.
Anyone know any Invisibility Charms?

Delphi/Hermione
Do we go – in her office?

Albus/Ron
She'll be coming to her office.

Delphi/Hermione
There's nowhere else.

**She tries the door. She tries it
again.**

Hermione **(from off)**
If you don't talk to me or Ginny
about it . . .

Scorpius/Harry
Stand back. Alohomora!

**He aims his wand at the door. The
door swings open. He grins –
delighted.**

Albus. Block her. It has to be you.

130

Act One Scene Eighteen

Harry **(from off)**
    What is there to say?

Albus/Ron
    Me. Why?

Delphi/Hermione
    Well, it can't be either of us can it?
We **are** them.

Hermione **(from off)**
    What you said was obviously wrong –
but – there are more factors at play
here than—

Albus/Ron
    But I can't . . . I can't . . .

**There's a small kerfuffle and then
Albus/Ron ends up standing outside
the door as Hermione and Harry
enter from off.**

Harry
    Hermione, I'm grateful for your
concern but there's no need—

Hermione
    Ron?

Albus/Ron
Surprise!!!

Hermione
What are you doing here?

Albus/Ron
Does a man need an excuse to see his wife?

He kisses Hermione firmly.

Harry
I should go . . .

Hermione
Harry. My point is whatever Draco says – the things you said to Albus . . . I don't think it'll do any of us any good for you to dwell on it . . .

Albus/Ron
Oh, you're talking about how Harry said sometimes he wished I— **(he corrects himself)** Albus weren't his son.

Hermione
Ron!

Act One   Scene Eighteen

Albus/Ron
    Better out than in, that's what I
say . . .

Hermione
    He'll know . . . we all say stuff we
don't mean. He knows that.

Albus/Ron
    But what if sometimes we say stuff
we do mean . . . what then?

Hermione
    Ron, now's not the time, honestly.

Albus/Ron
    Of course it isn't. Bye, bye darling.

**Albus/Ron watches her go,
hopeful she'll walk past her office and
away. But of course she doesn't. He
runs to block her before she enters
through her door. He blocks her once,
and then blocks her again, swinging
his hips to do so.**

Hermione
    Why are you blocking the entrance to
my office?

Albus/Ron
I'm not. Blocking. Anything.

She again makes for the door, he blocks her again.

Hermione
You are. Let me into my room, Ron.

Albus/Ron
Let's have another baby.

Hermione tries to dodge past him.

Hermione
What?

Albus/Ron
Or if not another baby, a holiday. I want a baby or a holiday and I'm going to insist on it. Shall we talk about it later, honey?

She tries to get into the room one final time, he blocks her with a kiss. It develops into quite a struggle.

Maybe with a drink in the Leaky Cauldron? Love you.

Hermione **(relenting)**
If there's another stink pellet in there then Merlin won't help you. Fine. We're due to update the Muggles anyway.

She exits. Harry exits with her.

Albus/Ron turns towards the door. She re-enters, this time, alone.

A baby – OR – a holiday? Some days you are off the scale you know that?

Albus/Ron
It's why you married me isn't it? My puckish sense of fun.

She exits again. He starts to open the door but again she re-enters, he slams it closed.

Hermione
I can taste fish. I told you to stay away from those fish finger sandwiches.

Albus/Ron
Right you are.

Part One

She exits. He checks she's gone and the relief floods out of him as he opens the door.

Act One
Scene Nineteen

Ministry of Magic, Hermione's Office

Scorpius/Harry and Delphi/Hermione are waiting on the other side of Hermione's office door as Albus/Ron enters – he slumps, exhausted.

Albus/Ron
This is all too weird.

Delphi/Hermione
You were impressive. Good blocking action.

Scorpius/Harry
I don't know whether to high-five you or frown at you for kissing your aunt about five hundred times!

Albus/Ron
Ron's an affectionate guy. I was trying to distract her, Scorpius. I did distract her.

Scorpius/Harry
And then there's what your dad said . . .

Delphi/Hermione
Boys . . . she will be back – we don't have long.

Albus/Ron **(to Scorpius/Harry)**
You heard that?

Delphi/Hermione
Where would Hermione hide a Time-Turner? **(She looks around the room and sees the bookcases.)** Search the bookcases.

They start to search.
Scorpius/Harry looks at his friend, concerned.

Scorpius/Harry
Why didn't you tell me?

Act One Scene Nineteen

Albus/Ron
My dad says he wishes I weren't his son. Hardly a conversation starter is it?

Scorpius/Harry tries to work out what to say.

Scorpius/Harry
I know the – Voldemort thing isn't – true – and – you know – but sometimes, I think I can see my dad thinking: how did I produce this?

Albus/Ron
Still better than my dad. I'm pretty sure he spends most of his time thinking: how can I give him back?

Delphi/Hermione tries to pull Scorpius/Harry towards the bookcases.

Delphi/Hermione
Maybe if we could concentrate on the matter at hand.

Scorpius/Harry
My point is – there's a reason – we're friends, Albus – a reason we found

each other, you know? And whatever this – adventure is about . . .

Then he spots a book on the shelf that makes him frown.

Have you seen the books on these shelves? There are some serious books here. Banned books. Cursed books.

Albus/Ron
How to distract Scorpius from difficult emotional issues. Take him to a library.

Scorpius/Harry
All the books from the Restricted Section and then some. **Magick Moste Evile, Fifteenth-Century Fiends. Sonnets of a Sorcerer** – that's not even allowed in Hogwarts!

Albus/Ron
Shadows and Spirits. The Nightshade Guide to Necromancy.

Delphi/Hermione
They are quite something aren't they . . .

Albus/Ron
   The True History of the Opal Fire.
**The Imperius Curse and How to
Abuse it**.

Scorpius/Harry
   And lookee here. Whoah. **My Eyes
and How to See Past Them** by Sybill
Trelawney. A book on divination.
Hermione Granger hates divination. This
is fascinating. This is a find . . .

   **He pulls the book from the shelf.
And it falls open. And speaks.**

Book
   The first is the fourth, a disappointing
mark

   You'll find it in parked but not in
park.

Scorpius/Harry
   Okay. A book that talks. Bit weird.

Book
   The second is the less fair of those
that walk on two legs.

   Grubby, hairy a disease of the egg.

And the third is both a mountain to climb and a route to take.

Albus/Ron
    It's a riddle. It's giving us a riddle.

Book
    A turn in the city, a glide through a lake.

Delphi/Hermione
    What have you done?

Scorpius/Harry
    I, uh, I opened a book. Something which has – in all my years on this planet – never been a particularly dangerous activity.

The books reach out and grab Albus. He only just eludes their grasp.

Albus/Ron
    What is that?

Delphi/Hermione
    She's weaponised it. She's weaponised her library. This is where the Time-Turner will be. Solve the riddle and we'll find it.

142

Act One   Scene Nineteen

Albus/Ron
The first is a fourth. You'll find it in parked, not in park. Ed – De—

The books start to try and swallow Delphi/Hermione.

Scorpius/Harry
The second is a disease of the egg, the less fair of those who walk on two legs . . .

Delphi/Hermione **(effusively)**
Men! De – men – tors. We need to find a book on Dementors (**the bookcase pulls her in**), Albus!

Albus/Ron
Delphi! What is going on?

Scorpius/Harry
Concentrate, Albus. Do what she said. Find a book on Dementors and be very careful.

Albus/Ron
Here. **Dominating Dementors: A True History of Azkaban**.

Part One

The book flies open and swings dangerously at Scorpius/Harry, who has to dodge out of the way. He falls hard against a bookcase which attempts to consume him.

Book
    I was born in a cage

    But smashed it with rage

    The Gaunt inside me

    Riddled me free

    Of that which would stop me to be.

Albus/Ron
    Voldemort.

Delphi plunges through the books, back as herself.

Delphi
    Work faster!

She's pulled back in screaming.

Albus/Ron
    Delphi! Delphi!

Act One Scene Nineteen

He tries to grab her hand, but she's gone.

Scorpius/Harry
She'd become herself again – did you notice?

Albus/Ron
No! Because I was more worried about her being eaten by a bookcase! Find. Something. Anything on him.

He finds a book.

The Heir of Slytherin? Do you think?

He pulls the book from the shelf, it pulls back, Albus/Ron is consumed by the bookcase.

Scorpius/Harry
Albus? Albus!!

But Albus/Ron is gone.

Okay. Not that. Voldemort. Voldemort. Voldemort.

He scans the shelves.

Marvolo: The Truth, this must be . . .

He pulls it open. Again it swings away, revealing a splintering light, and a deeper voice than previously heard.

Book
I am the creature you have not seen

I am you. I am me. The echo unforeseen.

Sometimes in front, sometimes behind,

A constant companion, for we are entwined.

Albus emerges from the books. As himself again.

Scorpius/Harry
Albus . . .

He tries to grab him.

Act One Scene Nineteen

Albus
    No. Just – thiiiiink.

Albus is violently pulled back into the bookcase.

Scorpius/Harry
    But I can't . . . an invisible echo, what is that? The only thing I'm good at is thinking and when I need to think – I can't.

The books pull him inside them; he's powerless. This is terrifying.

There's silence.

Then bang – a shower of books are released from the bookcase – and Scorpius re-emerges. Smashing the books aside.

Scorpius
    No! You don't! Sybill Trelawney. No!!!

He looks around, sunk but full of energy.

    This is all wrong. Albus? Can you

hear me? All this for a frigging Time-Turner. Think, Scorpius. Think.

Books try and grab him.

A constant companion. Sometimes behind. Sometimes in front. Hang on. I've missed it. Shadow. You're a shadow. **Shadows and Spirits**. It must be . . .

He climbs up the bookcase, which is horrifying as it rises up at him. Grabbing at him with his every step.

He pulls the book from the shelf. It comes out and the noise and chaos suddenly stop.

Is that—

Suddenly there's a smashing and Albus and Delphi fall out of the shelves and down to the floor.

We beat it. We beat the library.

Albus
Delphi, are you . . . ?

Act One   Scene Nineteen

Delphi
Wow. Quite a ride.

Albus notices the book Scorpius is holding to his chest.

Albus
Is that? Scorpius? What's inside that book?

Delphi
I think we should find out don't you?

Scorpius opens the book. In the centre of it – a spinning Time-Turner.

Scorpius
We've found the Time-Turner – I never thought we'd get this far.

Albus
Mate, now we've got this, the next stop is saving Cedric. Our journey has only just begun.

Scorpius
Only just begun and it's almost half-killed us. Good. This is going to be good.

Whispers rise to a roar. And we cut to black.

Interval

Part One

Act Two

Act Two
Scene One

Dream, Privet Drive, Cupboard Under the Stairs

Aunt Petunia
    Harry. Harry. These pots aren't clean. These pots are a disgrace. Harry Potter. Wake up.

Young Harry wakes to see Aunt Petunia bearing down on him.

Young Harry
    Aunt Petunia. What time is it?

Aunt Petunia
    Time enough. You know, when we agreed to take you in, we hoped we could improve you – build you – make you a decent human being. So I

suppose it's only ourselves we've got to <u>blame that you've</u> turned out – such a limp disappointment.

Young Harry
  I try—

Aunt Petunia
  Trying is not succeeding, though, is it? There are grease smears on the glasses. There are scuff marks on the pots. Now get up and go to the kitchen and get scrubbing.

He gets out of bed. There's a wet smear down the back of his trousers.

Oh no. Oh no. What have you done? You've wet the bed, again.

She pulls back the covers.

This is very unacceptable.

Young Harry
  I'm . . . sorry, I think I was having a nightmare.

Act Two Scene One

Aunt Petunia

You disgusting boy. Only animals wet themselves. Animals and disgusting little boys.

Young Harry

It was about my mum and dad. I think I saw them – I think I saw them – die?

Aunt Petunia

And why would I have the slightest bit of interest in that?

Young Harry

There was a man shouting Adkava Ad-something Acabra – Ad – and the noise of a snake hissing. I could hear my mum scream.

Aunt Petunia takes a moment to reset herself.

Aunt Petunia

If you were really reliving their death, all you'd hear would be a screech of brakes and a horrific thud. Your parents died in a car accident. You know that. I don't think your mother had even time to scream. Lord spare you the details more than that. Now strip those sheets, get in the kitchen and get scrubbing. I don't want to have to tell you again.

She exits with a bang.

And Young Harry is left holding the sheets.

And the stage contorts and trees rise as the dream twists into something else entirely.

Suddenly, Albus appears and stands looking at Young Harry.

And then right from the back of the room Parseltongue whispers around everyone.

He's coming. He's coming.

Words said with an unmistakeable voice. The voice of Voldemort . . .

Haaarry Pottttter . . .

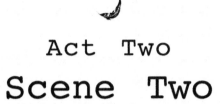

Act Two
Scene Two

Harry and Ginny Potter's House, Staircase

Harry wakes in the darkness, breathing deeply. His exhaustion palpable, his fear overwhelming.

Harry
Lumos.

Ginny enters, surprised by the light.

Ginny
Okay . . . ?

Harry
I was sleeping.

Ginny
　You were.

Harry
　You weren't. Any – news? Any owls
or . . . ?

Ginny
　None.

Harry
　I was dreaming – I was under the
stairs and then I – I heard him –
Voldemort – so clearly.

Ginny
　Voldemort?

Harry
　And then I saw – Albus. In red – he
was wearing Durmstrang robes.

Ginny
　Durmstrang robes?

Harry thinks.

Harry
　Ginny, I think I know where he is . . .

Act Two
Scene Three

Hogwarts, Headmistress'S Office

Harry and Ginny stand in Professor McGonagall's office.

Professor McGonagall
    And we don't know where in the Forbidden Forest?

Harry
    I haven't had a dream like it for years. But Albus was there. I know he was.

Ginny
    We need to get searching as quickly as possible.

Professor McGonagall
    I can give you Professor Longbottom

– his knowledge of plants might be
useful – and—

**Suddenly there is a rumble in the
chimney. Professor McGonagall
looks at it, concerned. Then
Hermione tumbles out.**

Hermione
    Is it true? Can I help?

Professor McGonagall
    Minister – this is quite unex-
pected . . .

Ginny
    That may be my fault – I persuaded
them to put out an emergency edition of
the **Daily Prophet**. Asking for volunteers.

Professor McGonagall
    Right. Very sensible. I expect . . .
there will be quite a few.

**Ron bursts in. Covered in soot.
Wearing a gravy-stained dinner napkin.**

Ron
    Have I missed anything – I couldn't

work out which Floo to travel to. Ended up in the kitchen somehow. **(Hermione glares as he pulls the napkin off himself.)** What?

Suddenly there is another rumble in the chimney and Draco comes down hard, surrounded by cascading soot and dust.

Everyone looks at him, surprised. He stands and brushes the soot off himself.

Draco
Sorry about your floor, Minerva.

Professor McGonagall
I dare say it's my fault for owning a chimney.

Harry
Quite a surprise to see you, Draco. I thought you didn't believe in my dreams.

Draco
I don't, but I do trust your luck. Harry Potter is always where the action

is at. And I need my son back with me
and safe.

Ginny
    Then let's get to the Forbidden Forest
and find them both.

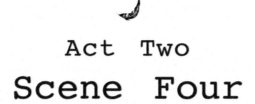

Act Two
Scene Four

Edge of the Forbidden Forest

Albus and Delphi face each other, holding wands.

Albus
Expelliarmus!

Delphi's wand flies through the air.

Delphi
You're getting it now. You're good at this.

She takes her wand back from him.

In a posh voice.

'You're a positively disarming young man.'

Albus
Expelliarmus!

Her wand flies back again.

Delphi
And we have a winner.

The two high-five.

Albus
I've never been good at spells.

Scorpius appears at the back of the stage. He looks at his friend talking to a girl – and part of him likes it and part of him doesn't.

Delphi
I was rubbish – and then something clicked. And it will for you too. Not that I'm a super witch or anything but I think you're becoming quite some wizard, Albus Potter.

Albus
Then you should stick around – teach me more—

Delphi
Of course I'm sticking around, we're friends aren't we?

Albus
Yes. Yes. Definitely friends. Definitely.

Delphi
Great. Wizzo!

Scorpius
What's wizzo?

Scorpius steps forward decisively.

Albus
Cracked the spell. I mean, it's pretty basic, but I was – well, I cracked it.

Scorpius **(over-enthusiastic, trying to join in)**
And I've found our way through to the school. Listen, are we sure this will work . . .

Delphi
    Yes!

Albus
    It's a brilliant plan. The secret to not
getting Cedric killed is to stop him
winning the Triwizard Tournament. If he
doesn't win, he can't be killed.

Scorpius
    And I understand that but . . .

Albus
    So we just need to mess up his
chances supremely badly in task one.
The first task is getting a golden egg
from a dragon – how did Cedric distract
the dragon—

**Delphi puts her hand in the
air. Albus grins and points at her.
These two are getting on really well
now.**

    Diggory.

Delphi
    —by transfiguring a stone into a dog.

Act Two Scene Four

Albus
    —well, a little Expelliarmus and he won't be able to do that.

Scorpius isn't enjoying the Delphi-Albus double act.

Scorpius
    Okay, two points, first point we're certain the dragon won't kill him?

Delphi
    It's always two points with him isn't it? Of course it won't. This is Hogwarts. They won't let damage happen to any of the champions.

Scorpius
    Okay, second **point** – more signifi-cant **point** – we're going back without any knowledge of whether we can travel back afterwards. Which is exciting. Maybe we should just – try going back an hour, say, first and then . . .

Delphi
    I'm sorry, Scorpius, we've no time to waste. Waiting here this close to the

school is just too dangerous – I'm sure they'll be looking for you and . . .

Albus
    She's right.

Delphi
    Now, you're going to need to wear these—

She pulls out two large paper bags. The boys pull out robes from them.

Albus
    But these are Durmstrang robes.

Delphi
    My uncle's idea. If you are in Hogwarts robes people will expect to know who you are. But there are two other schools competing at the Triwizard Tournament – and if you're in Durmstrang robes – well, you can fade into the background, can't you?

Albus
    Good thinking! Hang on, where are your robes?

Act Two   Scene Four

Delphi
Albus, I'm flattered, but I don't think I can pretend to be a student, do you? I'll just keep in the background, and pretend to be a – ooh, maybe I could pretend to be a dragon tamer. You're doing all the spell stuff anyway.

Scorpius looks at her and then at Albus.

Scorpius
You shouldn't come.

Delphi
What?

Scorpius
You're right. We don't need you for the spell. And if you can't wear student robes – you're too big a risk. Sorry, Delphi, you shouldn't come.

Delphi
But I have to – he's my cousin. Albus?

Albus
I think he's right. I'm sorry.

Delphi
What?

Albus
We won't mess up.

Delphi
But without me – you won't be able
to work the Time-Turner.

Scorpius
You taught us how to use the
Time-Turner.

Delphi is really upset.

Delphi
No. I won't let you do this . . .

Albus
You told your uncle to trust us. Now
it's your turn. The school is close now.
We should leave you here.

**Delphi looks at them both and
takes a deep breath. She nods to
herself and smiles.**

Delphi
Then go. But – just know this . . .
today you get an opportunity few are
given – today you get to change history
– to change time itself. But more than
all that, today you get the chance to
give an old man his son back.

**She smiles. She looks at Albus.
She leans down and gently kisses him
on both cheeks.**

**She walks away into the woodland.
Albus stares after her.**

Scorpius
She didn't kiss me – did you notice?
(He looks at his friend.) Are you okay,
Albus? You look a little pale. And red.
Pale and red at the same time.

Albus
Let's do this.

Act Two
Scene Five

The Forbidden Forest

The forest seems to grow bigger, thicker, and amongst the trees – people searching – looking for the missing wizards. But slowly people melt away until Harry is left alone.

He hears something.
He turns to his right.

Harry
    Albus? Scorpius? Albus?

And then he hears the sound of hooves. Harry is startled. He looks around for where the noise is coming from.

Act Two Scene Five

Suddenly Bane steps forward into the light. He is a magnificent centaur.

Bane
   Harry Potter.

Harry
   Good. You still recognise me, Bane.

Bane
   You've grown older.

Harry
   I have.

Bane
   But not wiser. For you trespass on our land.

Harry
   I have always respected the centaurs. We are not enemies. You fought bravely at the Battle of Hogwarts. And I fought beside you.

Bane
   I did my part. But for my herd, and our honour. Not for you. And after the battle, the forest was deemed centaur

land. And if you're on our land – without permission – then you are our enemy.

Harry
    My son is missing, Bane. I need help finding him.

Bane
    And he is here? In our forest?

Harry
    Yes.

Bane
    Then he is as stupid as you are.

Harry
    Can you help me Bane?

There's a pause. Bane looks down at Harry imperiously.

Bane
    I can only tell you what I know . . . but I tell you not for your benefit but for the benefit of my herd. The centaurs do not need another war.

Act Two Scene Five

Harry
Neither do we. What do you know?

Bane
I've seen your son, Harry Potter. Seen him in the movements of the stars.

Harry
You've seen him in the stars?

Bane
I can't tell you where he is. I can't tell you how you'll find him.

Harry
But you've seen something? You've divined something?

Bane
There is a black cloud around your son, a dangerous black cloud.

Harry
Around Albus?

Bane
A black cloud that may endanger us all. You'll find your son again, Harry

Potter. But then you could lose him forever.

He makes a sound like a horse's cry – and then makes hard away – leaving a bewildered Harry behind.

Harry begins to search again – now with even more fervour.

Harry
　Albus! Albus!

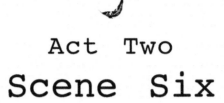

Act Two
Scene Six

Edge of the Forbidden Forest

Scorpius and Albus round a corner to be faced with a gap in the trees . . .

A gap through which is visible . . . a glorious light . . .

Scorpius
  And there it is . . .

Albus
  Hogwarts. Never seen this view of it before.

Scorpius
  Still get a tingle, don't you? When you see it?

Part One

**And revealed through the trees is
Hogwarts – a splendid mass of
bulbous buildings and towers.**

From the moment I first heard of it,
I was desperate to go. I mean, Dad
didn't much like it there but even the
way he described it . . . From the age
of ten I'd check the **Daily Prophet** first
thing every morning – certain some sort
of tragedy would have befallen it –
certain I wouldn't get to go.

Albus
And then you got there and it turned
out to be terrible after all.

Scorpius
Not for me.

Albus looks at his friend, shocked.

All I ever wanted to do was go to
Hogwarts and have a mate to get up to
mayhem with. Just like Harry Potter. And I
got his son. How crazily fortunate is that.

Albus
But I'm nothing like my dad.

Scorpius
You're better. You're my best friend, Albus. And this is mayhem to the nth degree. Which is great, thumbs-up great, it's just – I have got to say – I don't mind admitting – I am a tiny bit – just a tiny bit scared.

Albus looks at Scorpius and smiles.

Albus
You're my best friend too. And don't worry – I have a good feeling about this.

We hear Ron's voice from off – he's clearly in close proximity.

Ron
Albus? Albus!

Albus turns towards it, scared.

Albus
But we've got to go – now.

Albus takes the Time-Turner from Scorpius – he presses down upon it and the Time-Turner begins to

vibrate, and then explodes into a storm of movement.

And with it the stage starts to transform. The two boys look at it.

And there is a giant whoosh of light. A smash of noise.

And time stops. And then it turns over, thinks a bit, and begins spooling backwards, slow at first . . .

And then it speeds up.

Act Two
Scene Seven

Triwizard Tournament, Edge of the Forbidden Forest, 1994

Suddenly everything is a riot of noise as a crowd consumes Albus and Scorpius.

And suddenly 'the greatest showman on earth' (his words, not ours) is on stage, using Sonorus to amplify his voice, and . . . well . . . he's having a ball.

Ludo Bagman
    Ladies and gentlemen, boys and girls, I give you – the greatest – the fabulous – the one – and the only Triwizard Tournament.

There's a loud cheer.

If you're from Hogwarts. Give me a cheer.

There's a loud cheer.

If you're from Durmstrang – give me a cheer.

There's a loud cheer.

And if you're from Beauxbatons give me a cheer.

There's a slightly limp cheer.

Slightly less enthusiastic from the French there.

Scorpius **(smiling)**
This has worked. That's Ludo Bagman.

Ludo Bagman
And there they are. Ladies and gentlemen – boys and girls – I present to you – the reason why we're all here – The Champions. Representing Durmstrang, what eyebrows, what a gait,

what a boy, there's nothing he won't try on a broomstick, it's Viktor Krazy Krum.

Scorpius and Albus (who are really getting into playing the Durmstrang students now)
Go go Krazy Krum. Go go Krazy Krum.

Ludo Bagman
From the Beauxbatons Academy – zut alors, it's Fleur Delacour!

There's some polite applause.

And from Hogwarts not one but two students, he makes us all go weaky at the kneesy, he's Cedric Delicious Diggory.

The crowd go wild.

And then the other – you know him as the Boy Who Lived, I know him as the boy who keeps surprising us all . . .

Albus
That's my dad.

Ludo Bagman
Yes, it's Harry Plucky Potter.

There's cheering. Particularly from a nervous-looking girl at the edge of the crowd – this is Young Hermione (played by the same actress as plays Rose). It is noticeable that the cheering for Harry is slightly less than that for Cedric.

And now – silence please all. The – first – task. Retrieving a golden egg. From a nest of – ladies and gentlemen, boys and girls, I give you – dragons. And guiding the dragons – Charlie Weasley.

There are more cheers.

Young Hermione
   If you're going to stand so close I'd rather you didn't breathe on me quite so much.

Scorpius
   Rose? What are you doing here?

Young Hermione
   Who's Rose? And what's happened to your accent?

Act Two Scene Seven

Albus **(with a bad accent)**
Sorry. Hermione. He's got you mixed up with someone else.

Young Hermione
How do you know my name?

Ludo Bagman
And with no time to lose, let's bring out our first champion – facing a Swedish Short-Snout, I give you – Cedric Diggory!

A dragon roar distracts Young Hermione, and Albus readies his wand.

And Cedric Diggory has entered the stage. And he seems ready. Scared but ready. He dodges this way. He dodges that. The girls swoon as he dives for cover. They cry as one: don't damage our Diggory, Mr Dragon.

Scorpius looks concerned.

Scorpius
Albus, something is going wrong. The Time-Turner, it's shaking.

A ticking begins, an incessant, dangerous, ticking. It's coming from the Time-Turner.

Ludo Bagman
    And Cedric skirts left and he dives right – and he readies his wand – what has this young, brave, handsome man got up his sleevies now—

Albus **(extending his wand)**
    Expelliarmus!

Cedric's wand is summoned to Albus's hand.

Ludo Bagman
    —but no, what's this? Is it Dark Magic or is it something else entirely – Cedric Diggory is disarmed—

Scorpius
    Albus, I think the Time-Turner – something is wrong . . .

The Time-Turner's ticking gets louder still.

Act Two   Scene Seven

Ludo Bagman
It's all going wrong for Diggors. This could be the end of the task for him. The end of the tournament.

Scorpius grabs Albus.

There's a crescendo in the ticking and a flash.

And time is turned back to the present, with Albus hollering in pain.

Scorpius
Albus! Did it hurt you? Albus are you—

Albus
What happened?

Scorpius
There must be some limit – the Time-Turner must have some kind of **time** limit . . .

Albus
Do you think we've done it? Do you think we've changed anything?

**Suddenly the stage is invaded
from all sides by Harry, Ron (who
now has a side parting and whose
wardrobe choices have become
rather more staid), Ginny and
Draco. Scorpius looks at them all –
and slips the Time-Turner back into
his pocket. Albus looks at them
rather more blankly – he's in a lot
of pain.**

Ron
> I told you. I told you I saw them.

Scorpius
> I think we're about to find out.

Albus
> Hello, Dad. Is something wrong?

**Harry looks at his son
disbelievingly.**

Harry
> Yes. You could say that.

**Albus collapses on to the floor.
Harry and Ginny rush to help.**

Act Two
Scene Eight

Hogwarts,
Hospital Wing

Albus is asleep in a hospital bed. Harry sits, troubled, beside him. Above them is a picture of a concerned, kindly man. Harry rubs his eyes, stands and walks around the room, stretching his back.

And then he meets eyes with the painting. Which looks startled to be spotted. And Harry looks startled back.

Harry
  Professor Dumbledore.

Dumbledore
  Good evening, Harry.

Harry
I've missed you. Whenever I've dropped in on the Headmistress lately, your frame's been empty.

Dumbledore
Ah, well, I do like to pop into my other portraits now and then. **(He looks at Albus.)** Will he be all right?

Harry
He's been out twenty-four hours, mostly in order so Madam Pomfrey could reset his arm. She said it was the strangest thing . . . it's like it was broken twenty years ago and allowed to set in the 'most contrary' of directions. She says he'll be fine.

Dumbledore
A difficult thing, I imagine, to watch your child in pain.

Harry looks up at Dumbledore, and then down at Albus.

Harry
I've never asked how you felt about me naming him after you, have I?

Act Two Scene Eight

Dumbledore
Candidly, Harry, it seemed a great weight to place upon the poor boy.

Harry
I need your help. I need your advice. Bane says Albus is in danger. How do I protect my son, Dumbledore?

Dumbledore
You ask me, of all people, how to protect a boy in terrible danger? We cannot protect the young from harm. Pain must and will come.

Harry
So I'm supposed to stand and watch?

Dumbledore
No. You're supposed to teach him how to meet life.

Harry
How? He won't listen.

Dumbledore
Perhaps he's waiting for you to see him clearly.

Part One

Harry frowns as he tries to digest this.

(With sensitivity.) It is a portrait's curse and blessing to . . . hear things. At the school, at the Ministry, I hear people talking . . .

Harry
   And what is the gossip about me and my son?

Dumbledore
   Not gossip. Concern. That you two are struggling. That he's difficult. That he is angry with you. I have formed the impression that – perhaps – you are blinded by your love for him.

Harry
   Blinded?

Dumbledore
   You must see him as he is, Harry. You must look for what's wounding him.

Harry
   Haven't I seen him as he is? What's

wounding my son? **(He thinks.)** Or is it who's wounding my son?

Albus **(mumbles in his sleep)**
  Dad . . .

Harry
  This black cloud, it's someone isn't it? Not something?

Dumbledore
  Ah really, what does my opinion matter any more? I am paint and memory, Harry, paint and memory. And I never had a son.

Harry
  But I need your advice.

Albus
  Dad?

  Harry looks at Albus and then back at Dumbledore. But Dumbledore is gone.

Harry
  No, where have you gone now?

Albus
    We're in – the hospital wing?

Harry turns his attention back to Albus.

Harry **(discombobulated)**
    Yes. And you're – you will be fine.
For recuperation, Madam Pomfrey wasn't
sure what to prescribe and said you
should probably eat lots of – chocolate.
Actually, do you mind if I have some?
I've got something to tell you and I
don't think you'll like it.

Albus looks at his dad, what does he have to say? He decides not to engage.

Albus
    Okay. I think.

Harry takes some chocolate. He eats a big chunk. Albus looks at his dad, confused.

    Better?

Harry
  Much.

He holds out the chocolate to his son. Albus takes a piece. Father and son munch together.

The arm, how does it feel?

Albus flexes his arm.

Albus
  It feels great.

Harry **(soft)**
  Where did you go Albus? I can't tell you what it did to us – your mum was worried sick . . .

Albus looks up, he is a great liar.

Albus
  We decided we didn't want to come to school. We thought we could start again – in the Muggle world – we discovered we were wrong. We were coming back to Hogwarts when you found us.

Harry
    In Durmstrang robes?

Albus
    The robes were . . . the whole thing
– Scorpius and I – we didn't think.

Harry
    And why . . . why did you run?
Because of me? Because of what I said?

Albus
    I don't know. Hogwarts isn't actually
that pleasant a place when you don't fit in.

Harry
    And did Scorpius – encourage you to
– go?

Albus
    Scorpius? No.

**Harry looks at Albus, trying to
see almost an aura around him,
thinking deeply.**

Harry
    I need you to stay away from
Scorpius Malfoy.

Act Two   Scene Eight

Albus
What? Scorpius?

Harry
I don't know how you became friends in the first place, but you did – and now – I need you to—

Albus
My best friend? My only friend?

Harry
He's dangerous.

Albus
Scorpius? Dangerous? Have you met him? Dad, if you honestly think he's the son of Voldemort—

Harry
I don't know what he is, I just know you need to stay away from him. Bane told me—

Albus
Who's Bane?

Harry
A centaur with profound divination

197

skills. He said there's a black cloud around you and—

Albus
 A black cloud?

Harry
 And I have very good reason to believe that Dark Magic is in a resurgence and I need to keep you safe from it. Safe from him. Safe from Scorpius.

Albus hesitates a moment, and then his face strengthens.

Albus
 And if I won't? Stay away from him?

Harry looks at his son, thinking quickly.

Harry
 There's a map. It used to be used for those wanting to get up to no good. Now we're going to use it to keep an eye – a permanent eye – on you. Professor McGonagall will watch your every movement. Any time you are seen together – she'll come flying – any time

you attempt to leave Hogwarts – she'll fly. I expect you to go to your lessons, none of which you will now share with Scorpius, and between times, you will stay in the Gryffindor common room!

Albus
You can't make me go into Gryffindor! I'm Slytherin!

Harry
Don't play games Albus, you know what house you are. If she finds you with Scorpius – I will fix you with a spell – which will allow me eyes and ears into your every movement, your every conversation. In the meantime, investigations will begin in my department as to his true heritage.

Albus (starting to cry)
But Dad – you can't – that's just not . . .

Harry
I thought for a long time I wasn't a good enough dad for you because you didn't like me. It's only now I realise that I don't need you to like me, I need

you to obey me because I'm your dad
and I do know better. I'm sorry, Albus.
It has to be this way.

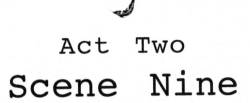

Act Two
Scene Nine

Hogwarts, Staircases

**Albus pursues Harry
across the stage.**

Albus
　　What if I run? I'll run.

Harry
　　Albus, get back in bed.

Albus
　　I'll run away again.

Harry
　　No. You won't.

Albus

I will – and this time I'll make sure
Ron can't find us.

Ron

Do I hear my name?

**Ron enters on a staircase, his side
parting now super-aggressive, his
robes just a little bit too short, his
clothes now spectacularly staid.**

Albus

Uncle Ron! Thank Dumbledore. If
ever we needed one of your jokes it's
now . . .

Ron frowns, confused.

Ron

Jokes? I don't know any jokes.

Albus

Of course you do. You run a joke
shop.

Ron **(now supremely confused)**

A joke shop? Well now. Anyway I'm
pleased I caught you . . . I was going to

202

bring some sweets – for a, uh, sort of, a, get well soon, but, uh . . . actually Padma – she thinks about things a lot more – deeply than I do – and she thought it'd be nicer for you to get something useful for school. So we got you a – set of quills. Yes. Yes. Yes. Look at these bad boys. Top of the range.

Albus
    Who's Padma?

Harry frowns at Albus.

Harry
    Your aunt.

Albus
    I have an Aunt Padma?

Ron
    (To Harry) Taken a Confundus Charm to the head, has he? **(To Albus)** My wife, Padma. You remember. Talks slightly too close to your face, smells a bit minty. **(Leans in.)** Padma, mother of Panju! **(To Harry.)** That's why I'm here, of course. Panju. He's in trouble again. I wanted to just send a Howler but Padma

insisted I come in person. I don't know why. He just laughs at me.

Albus
But . . . you're married to Hermione.

Beat. Ron doesn't understand this at all.

Ron
Hermione? No. Nooooo. Merlin's beard.

Harry
Albus has also forgotten that he was sorted into Gryffindor. Conveniently.

Ron
Yes, well, sorry, old chap, but you're a Gryffindor.

Albus
But how did I get sorted into Gryffindor?

Ron
You persuaded the Sorting Hat, don't you remember? Panju bet you that you couldn't get into Gryffindor if your life

depended on it, so you chose Gryffindor to spite him. I can't blame you, **(dryly)** we'd all like to wipe the smile off his face sometimes wouldn't we? **(Terrified.)** Please don't tell Padma I said that.

Albus
Who's Panju?

Ron and Harry stare at Albus.

Ron
Bloody hell, you're really not yourself are you? Anyway, better go, before I'm sent a Howler myself.

He stumbles on, not even an inch of the man he was.

Albus
But that doesn't . . . make sense.

Harry
Albus, whatever you're feigning, it isn't working, I will not change my mind.

Albus
Dad, you have two choices, either you take me to—

Harry
   No, you're the one with the choice
Albus. You do this, or you get in
deeper – much deeper – trouble, do
you understand?

Scorpius
   Albus? You're okay. That's fantastic.

Harry
   He's completely cured. And we've got
to go.

   **Albus looks up at Scorpius and
his heart breaks. He walks on.**

Scorpius
   Are you mad at me? What's going
on?

   **Albus stops and turns to
Scorpius.**

Albus
   Did it work? Did any of it work?

Scorpius
   No . . . but, Albus—

Harry
    Albus. Whatever gibberish you're talking, you need to stop it, now. This is your final warning.

Albus looks torn between his dad and his friend.

Albus
    I can't, okay?

Scorpius
    You can't what?

Albus
    Just – we'll be better off without each other, okay?

Scorpius is left looking up after him. Heartbroken.

Act Two
Scene Ten

Hogwarts, Headmistress'S Office

Professor McGonagall is full of unhappiness, Harry is full of purpose, Ginny is not sure what she's supposed to be.

Professor McGonagall
I'm not sure this is what the Marauder's Map was intended for.

Harry
If you see them together, then get to them as quickly as possible, and keep them separate.

Professor McGonagall
Harry, are you sure this is the right decision? Because far be it from me to

doubt the wisdom of the centaurs but
Bane is an extremely angry centaur
and . . . it's not beyond him to twist the
constellations for his own ends.

Harry
    I trust Bane. Albus is to stay away
from Scorpius. For his sake, and others'.

Ginny
    I think what Harry means is . . .

Harry **(with finality)**
    The Professor knows what I mean.

**Ginny looks at Harry, surprised
that he'd talk to her that way.**

Professor McGonagall
    Albus has been checked by the
greatest witches and wizards in the
country and no one can find or sense a
hex or a curse.

Harry
    And Dumbledore – Dumbledore said—

Professor McGonagall
    What?

Part One

Harry
    His portrait. We spoke. He said some things which made sense—

Professor McGonagall
    Dumbledore is dead, Harry. And I've told you before, portraits don't represent even half of their subjects.

Harry
    He said love had blinded me.

Professor McGonagall
    A headteacher's portrait is a memoir. It is supposed to be a support mechanism for the decisions I have to make. But I was advised as I took this job to not mistake the painting for the person. And you would be well-advised to do the same.

Harry
    But he was right. I see it now.

Professor McGonagall
    Harry, you've been put under enormous pressure, the loss of Albus, the search for him, the fears as to what your scar might mean. But trust me

when I tell you, you are making a
mistake—

Harry
    Albus didn't like me before. He might
not like me again. But he will be safe.
With the greatest respect, Minerva – you
don't have children—

Ginny
    Harry!

Harry
    —you don't understand.

Professor McGonagall **(deeply
hurt)**
    I'd hope that a lifetime spent in the
teaching profession would mean—

Harry
    This map will reveal to you where my
son is at all times – I expect you to use
it. And if I hear you don't – then I will
come down on this school as hard as I
can – using the full force of the Ministry
– is that understood?

Professor McGonagall **(bewildered by this vitriol)**
Perfectly.

Ginny looks at Harry, unsure of what he's become. He doesn't look back.

———

Act Two
Scene Eleven

Hogwarts, Defence Against the Dark Arts Class

Albus enters the classroom, slightly unsure.

Hermione
Ah yes. Our train absconder. Finally joining us.

Albus
Hermione?

He looks amazed. Hermione is standing at the front of the lesson.

Hermione
Professor Granger I believe is my name, Potter.

Part One

Albus
What are you doing here?

Hermione
Teaching. For my sins. What are you doing here? Learning I hope.

Albus
But you're . . . you're . . . Minister for Magic.

Hermione
Been having those dreams again have you Potter? Today we're going to look at Patronus Charms.

Albus (amazed)
You're our Defence Against the Dark Arts teacher?

There are titters.

Hermione
Losing patience now. Ten points from Gryffindor for stupidity.

Polly Chapman (standing, full of affront)
No. No. He's doing it deliberately.

Act Two Scene Eleven

He hates Gryffindor and everyone
knows it.

Hermione

Sit down Polly Chapman before this
gets even worse. **(Polly sighs and
then sits.)** And I suggest you join her,
Albus. And end this charade.

Albus

But you're not this mean.

Hermione

And that's twenty points from
Gryffindor to assure Albus Potter that I
am this mean.

Yann Fredericks

If you don't sit down right now,
Albus . . .

Albus sits.

Albus

Can I just say—

Hermione

No, you can't. Just keep quiet
Potter, otherwise you'll lose what limited

popularity you already have. Now who can tell me what a Patronus is? No? No one. You really are a most disappointing bunch.

Hermione smiles a thin smile. She really is quite mean.

Albus
No. This is stupid. Where's Rose? She'll tell you that you're being ridiculous.

Hermione
Who's Rose? Your invisible friend?

Albus
Rose Granger-Weasley! Your daughter! **(He realises.)** Of course . . . because you and Ron aren't married Rose—

There's giggling.

Hermione
How dare you! Fifty points from Gryffindor. And I assure you if anyone interrupts me again it'll be a hundred points . . .

She stares around the room. No one moves a muscle.

Good. A Patronus is a magical charm, a projection of all your most positive feelings and takes the shape of the animal with whom you share the deepest affinity. It is a gift of light. If you can conjure a Patronus, you can protect yourself against the world. Which, in some of our cases, seems like a necessity sooner rather than later.

———

Act Two
Scene Twelve

Hogwarts, Staircases

**Albus walks up a staircase.
Looking around as he does.**

**He doesn't see anything.
He exits. The staircases
move in almost a dance.**

**Scorpius enters behind him.
He thinks he's seen Albus,
he realises he isn't there.**

**He slumps down to the floor
as the staircase sweeps around.**

**Madam Hooch enters and walks
up the staircase. At the top, she
gestures for Scorpius to move.**

**He does. And slopes off –
his abject loneliness clear.**

**Albus enters and walks
up one staircase.**

**Scorpius enters and
walks up another.**

**The staircases meet.
The two boys look at each other.**

Lost and hopeful – all at once.

**And then Albus looks away
and the moment is broken – and
with it, possibly, the friendship.**

**And now the staircases part – the
two look at each other – one full
of guilt – the other full of pain –
both full of unhappiness.**

Act Two
Scene Thirteen

Harry and Ginny Potter's House, Kitchen

Ginny and Harry watch each other warily. There is an argument due, and both of them know it.

Harry
  This is the right decision.

Ginny
  You almost sound convinced.

Harry
  You told me to be honest with him, but actually I needed to be honest with myself, trust what my heart was telling me . . .

Act Two Scene Thirteen

Ginny

Harry, you have one of the greatest hearts of any wizard who ever lived, and I do not believe your heart told you to do this.

They hear a knock on the door.

Saved by the door.

She exits.

After a moment, Draco enters, consumed by anger but hiding it well.

Draco

I can't stay long. I won't need long.

Harry

How can I help?

Draco

I'm not here to antagonise you. But my son is in tears and I am his father and so I am here to ask why you would keep apart two good friends.

Harry

I'm not keeping them apart.

Draco
You've changed school timetables, you've threatened both teachers and Albus himself. Why?

Harry looks at Draco carefully and then turns away.

Harry
I have to protect my son.

Draco
From Scorpius?

Harry
Bane told me he sensed a darkness around my son. Near my son.

Draco
What are you implying, Potter?

Harry turns and looks Draco dead in the eye.

Harry
Are you sure . . . are you really sure he's yours Draco?

There's a deadly silence.

222

Act Two Scene Thirteen

Draco
 You take that back . . . right now.

But Harry doesn't take it back. So Draco takes his wand out.

Harry
 You do not want to do this.

Draco
 Yes I do.

Harry
 I don't want to hurt you, Draco.

Draco
 How interesting, because I do want to hurt you.

The two square up. And then release their wands.

Draco and Harry
 Expelliarmus!

Their wands repel and then break apart.

Draco
    Incarcerous!

**Harry dodges a blast from Draco's
wand.**

Harry
    Tarantallegra!

**Draco throws himself out of the
way.**

Harry
    You've been practising, Draco.

Draco
    And you've got sloppy, Potter.
Densaugeo!

**Harry just manages to get out of
the way.**

Harry
    Rictusempra!

**Draco uses a chair to block the
blast.**

Draco
  Flipendo!

Harry is sent twirling through the air. Draco laughs.

  Keep up, old man.

Harry
  We're the same age, Draco.

Draco
  I wear it better.

Harry
  Brachiabindo!

Draco is bound tightly.

Draco
  That really the best you got?
Emancipare!

Draco releases his own binds.

  Levicorpus!

Harry has to throw himself out of the way.

Mobilicorpus! Oh, this is too much fun . . .

Draco bounces Harry up and down on the table. And then as Harry rolls away, Draco jumps on to the table – he readies his wand, but as he does Harry hits him with a spell . . .

Harry
Obscuro!

Draco releases himself from his blindfold as soon as it hits.

The two square up – Harry throws a chair.

Draco ducks underneath it and slows the chair with his wand.

Ginny
I only left this room three minutes ago!

She looks at the mess of the kitchen. She looks at the chairs suspended in the air. She signals them back to the floor with her wand.

(Drier than dry.) What did I miss?

Act Two
Scene Fourteen

Hogwarts, Staircases

Scorpius walks unhappily down a staircase.

Delphi scurries in from the other side.

Delphi
So – technically – I shouldn't be here.

Scorpius
Delphi?

Delphi
In fact, technically I'm endangering our entire operation . . . which is not . . . well, I'm not a natural risk-taker as you know. I've never been to

Hogwarts. Pretty lax security here isn't there? And so many portraits. And corridors. And ghosts! This half-headless strange-looking ghost told me where I could find you, can you believe that?

Scorpius
    You've never been to Hogwarts?

Delphi
    I was – unwell – as a child – for a few years. Other people got to go – I did not.

Scorpius
    You were too – ill? I'm sorry, I didn't know that.

Delphi
    I don't advertise the fact – I prefer not to be seen as a tragic case, you know?

This registers with Scorpius. He looks up to say something but Delphi suddenly ducks from view as a student walks past. Scorpius tries to look casual until the student passes.

Have they gone?

Act Two Scene Fourteen

Scorpius
Delphi, maybe it is too dangerous for you to be here—

Delphi
Well – someone's got to do something about this.

Scorpius
Delphi, none of it worked, time-turning, we failed.

Delphi
I know. Albus owled me. The history books changed but not enough – Cedric still died. In fact, failing the first task only made him more determined to win the second.

Scorpius
And Ron and Hermione have gone completely skewwhiff – and I still haven't figured out why.

Delphi
And that's why Cedric has to wait. It's all become quite confused and you're entirely right to be keeping hold of the Time-Turner, Scorpius. But what I meant

was – someone's got to do something about the two of you.

Scorpius
    Oh.

Delphi
    You're best friends. Every owl he sends I can feel your absence. He's destroyed by it.

Scorpius
    Sounds like he's found a shoulder to cry on. How many owls has he sent you now?

Delphi smiles softly.

    Sorry. That's – I didn't mean – I just – don't understand what's going on. I've tried to see him, talk to him, but every time I do he runs off.

Delphi
    You know, I didn't have a best friend when I was your age. I wanted one. Desperately. When I was younger I even invented one but—

Act Two   Scene Fourteen

Scorpius
I had one of those too. Called Flurry. We fell out over the correct rules of Gobstones.

Delphi
Albus needs you, Scorpius. That's a wonderful thing.

Scorpius
He needs me to do what?

Delphi
That's the thing isn't it? About friend-ships. You don't know what he needs. You only know he needs it. Find him Scorpius. You two – you belong together.

———

Act Two
Scene Fifteen

Harry and Ginny Potter's House, Kitchen

Harry and Draco sit far apart. Ginny stands between them.

Draco
Sorry about your kitchen, Ginny.

Ginny
Oh, it's not my kitchen. Harry does most of the cooking.

Draco
I can't talk to him either. Scorpius. Especially since – Astoria has gone. I can't even talk about how losing her has affected him. As hard as I try, I can't

reach him. You can't talk to Albus. I can't talk to Scorpius. That's what this is about. Not about my son being evil. Because as much as you might take the word of a haughty centaur, you know the power of friendship.

Harry
    Draco, whatever you may think—

Draco
    I always envied you them you know – Weasley and Granger. I had—

Ginny
    Crabbe and Goyle.

Draco
    Two lunks who wouldn't know one end of a broomstick from another. You – the three of you – you shone you know? You liked each other. You had fun. I envied you those friendships more than anything else.

Ginny
    I envied them too.

Harry looks at Ginny, surprised.

Harry
I need to protect him—

Draco
My father thought he was protecting me. Most of the time. I think you have to make a choice – at a certain point – of the man you want to be. And I tell you that at that time you need a parent or a friend. And if you've learnt to hate your parent by then and you have no friends . . . then you're all alone. And being alone – that's so hard. I was alone. And it sent me to a truly dark place. For a long time. Tom Riddle was also a lonely child. You may not understand that Harry, but I do – and I think Ginny does too.

Ginny
He's right.

Draco
Tom Riddle didn't emerge from his dark place. And so Tom Riddle became Lord Voldemort. Maybe the black cloud Bane saw was Albus's loneliness. His pain. His hatred. Don't lose the boy. You'll regret it. And so will he. Because

he needs you, and Scorpius, whether or not he now knows it.

Harry looks at Draco, he thinks.

He opens his mouth to speak. He thinks.

Ginny
Harry. Will you get the Floo powder or shall I?

Harry looks up at his wife.

———

Act Two
Scene Sixteen

Hogwarts, Library

Scorpius arrives in the library. He looks left and right. And then he sees Albus. And Albus sees him.

Scorpius
Hi.

Albus
Scorpius. I can't . . .

Scorpius
I know. You're in Gryffindor now. You don't want to see me now. But here I am anyway. Talking to you.

Albus
Well, I can't talk, so—

Act Two Scene Sixteen

Scorpius

You have to. You think you can just ignore everything that's happened? The world has gone crazy, have you noticed?

Albus

I know, okay? Ron's gone strange. Hermione's a professor, it's all wrong but—

Scorpius

And Rose doesn't exist.

Albus

I know. Look, I don't understand everything, but you can't be here.

Scorpius

Because of what we did, Rose wasn't even born. Do you remember being told about the Triwizard Tournament Yule Ball? All the four Triwizard champions took a partner. Your dad took Parvati Patil, Viktor Krum took—

Albus

Hermione. And Ron got jealous and behaved like a prat.

Scorpius
    Only he didn't. I found Rita Skeeter's
book about them. And it's very different.
Ron took Hermione to the ball.

Albus
    What?

Polly Chapman
    Ssshhh!

**Scorpius looks at Polly and
drops his volume.**

Scorpius
    As friends. And they danced in a
friendly way, and it was nice, and then
he danced with Padma Patil and that
was nicer, and they started dating and
he changed a bit and then they got
married and meanwhile Hermione
became a—

Albus
    —psychopath.

Scorpius
    Hermione was supposed to go to
that ball with Krum – do you know why

she didn't? Because she had suspicions
the two strange Durmstrang boys she
met before the first task were somehow
involved in the disappearance of
Cedric's wand. She believed we, under
Viktor's orders, cost Cedric the first
task . . .

Albus
   Wow.

Scorpius
   And without Krum, Ron never got
jealous and that jealousy was all-impor-
tant and so Ron and Hermione stayed
very good friends but never fell in love –
never got married – **never had Rose.**

Albus
   So that's why Dad's so – did he
change too?

Scorpius
   I'm pretty sure your dad is exactly the
same. Head of Magical Law Enforcement.
Married to Ginny. Three kids.

Albus
   So why is he being such a—

A Librarian enters at the back of the room.

Scorpius
Have you heard me, Albus? This is bigger than you and your dad. Professor Croaker's law – the furthest someone can go back in time without the possibility of serious harm to the traveller or time itself is five hours. And we went back years. The smallest moment, the smallest change, it creates ripples. And we – we've created really bad ripples. Rose was never born because of what we did. Rose.

Librarian
Ssshhh!

Albus thinks quickly.

Albus
Fine, let's go back – fix it. Get Cedric and Rose back.

Scorpius
. . . is the wrong answer.

Act Two   Scene Sixteen

Albus
You've still got the Time-Turner, right?
No one found it?

**Scorpius takes it out of his
pocket.**

Scorpius
Yes, but . . .

Albus snatches it from his hand.

No. Don't . . . Albus. Don't you
understand how bad things could get?

**Scorpius grabs for the Time-
Turner, Albus pushes him back, they
wrestle inexpertly.**

Albus
Things need fixing, Scorpius. Cedric
still needs saving. Rose needs bringing
back. We'll be more careful. Whatever
Croaker says, trust me, trust us. We'll
get it right this time.

Scorpius
No. We won't. Give it back, Albus!
Give it back!

Part One

Albus
I can't. This is too important.

Scorpius
Yes it's too important – for us. We're not good at this stuff. We'll get it wrong.

Albus
Who's saying that we'll get it wrong?

Scorpius
I say. Because that's **what we do**. We mess things up. We lose. We're losers, true and total losers. Haven't you realised that yet?

Albus finally gets the upper hand and pins Scorpius to the ground.

Albus
Well, I wasn't a loser before I met you.

Scorpius
Albus, whatever you've got to prove to your dad – this isn't the way—

Albus
I don't have anything to prove to my

dad. I've got to save Cedric to save Rose. And maybe, without you holding me back, I can make a proper go of it.

Scorpius
Without me? Oh poor Albus Potter. With his chip on his shoulder. Poor Albus Potter. So sad.

Albus
What are you saying?

Scorpius **(exploding)**
Try my life! People look at you because your dad's the famous Harry Potter, saviour of the wizarding world. People look at me because they think my dad is Voldemort. Voldemort.

Albus
Don't even—

Scorpius
Can you even slightly imagine what that's like? Have you even ever tried? No. Because you can't see beyond the end of your nose. Because you can't see beyond the end of your stupid thing with your dad. He will always be Harry Potter,

you know that right? And you will always be his son. And I know it's hard, and the other kids are awful but you have to learn to be okay with that, because – there are worse things, okay?

Beat.

There was a moment I was excited, when I realised time was different, a moment when I thought maybe my mum hadn't got sick. Maybe my mum wasn't dead. But no, turns out, she was. I'm still the child of Voldemort, without a mother, giving sympathy to the boy who doesn't ever give anything back. So I'm sorry if I've ruined your life because I tell you – you wouldn't have a chance of ruining mine – it was already ruined. You just didn't make it better. Because you're a terrible – the most terrible – friend.

Albus digests this. He sees what he's done to his friend.

Professor McGonagall **(from off)**
Albus? Albus Potter. Scorpius Malfoy. Are you in there – together? Because I advise you not to be.

Act Two Scene Sixteen

Albus looks at Scorpius, he pulls a cloak from his bag.

Albus
Quick. We need to hide.

Scorpius
What?

Albus
Scorpius, look at me.

Scorpius
That's the Invisibility Cloak? Isn't it James's?

Albus
If she finds us, we'll be forced apart forever. Please. I didn't understand. Please.

Professor McGonagall **(from off, trying to give them every chance)**
I am about to enter.

Professor McGonagall comes into the room, the Marauder's Map in her hands. The boys disappear beneath the cloak. She looks around exasperated.

Well, where have they – I never
wanted this thing and now it's playing
tricks on me.

**She thinks. She looks back at the
map. She identifies where they should
be. She looks around the room.
Objects move as the boys invisibly
move past them. She sees where
they're heading, she makes to block
them. But they skirt around her.**

Unless. Unless . . . your father's cloak.

**She looks back at the map, she
looks at the boys. She smiles to
herself.**

Well, if I didn't see you, I didn't see
you.

**She exits. The two boys remove
the cloak. They sit in silence for a
moment.**

Albus
Yes, I stole this from James. He's
remarkably easy to steal from, his trunk
combination is the date he got his first

246

broom. I've found the cloak made avoiding bullies easier.

Scorpius nods.

I'm sorry – about your mum. I know we don't talk about her enough – but I hope you know – I'm sorry – it's rubbish – what happened to her – to you.

Scorpius
    Thanks.

Albus
    My dad said – said that you were this dark cloud around me. My dad started to think – and I just knew I had to stay away, and if I didn't, Dad said he would—

Scorpius
    Your dad thinks the rumours are true – I am the son of Voldemort?

Albus **(nods)**
    His department are currently investigating it.

Scorpius
    Good. Let them. Sometimes – some-

times I find myself thinking – maybe they're true too.

Albus
  No. They're not true. And I'll tell you why. Because I don't think Voldemort is capable of having a kind son – and you're kind, Scorpius. To the depths of your belly, to the tips of your fingers. I truly believe Voldemort – Voldemort couldn't have a child like you.

Beat. Scorpius is moved by this.

Scorpius
  That's nice – that's a nice thing to say.

Albus
  And it's something I should have said a long time ago. In fact, you're probably the best person I know. And you don't – you couldn't – hold me back – you make me stronger – and when Dad forced us apart – without you—

Scorpius
  I didn't much like my life without you in it either.

Albus
   And I know I'll always be Harry
Potter's son – and I will sort that out in
my head – and I know compared to you
my life is pretty good really and that he
and I are comparatively lucky and—

Scorpius **(interrupting)**
   Albus, as apologies go this is wonderfully fulsome, but you're starting to talk
more about **you** than **me** again, so probably better to quit while you're ahead.

**Albus smiles and stretches out a
hand.**

Albus
   Friends?

Scorpius
   Always.

**Scorpius extends his hand, Albus
pulls Scorpius up into a hug.**

That's the second time you've done
that.

The two boys break apart and smile.

Albus

But I'm pleased we had this argument because it's given me a really
good idea.

Scorpius

About what?

Albus

It involves the second task. And
humiliation.

Scorpius

You're still talking about going back
in time? Have we been having the same
conversation?

Albus

You're right – we are losers. We're
brilliant at losing and so we should be
using our own knowledge here. Our own
powers. Losers are taught to be losers.
And there's only one way to teach a loser
– and we know that better than anyone –
humiliation. We need to humiliate him. So
in the second task that's what we'll do.

**Scorpius thinks – for a long time
– and then smiles.**

Act Two Scene Sixteen

Scorpius
    That's a really good strategy.

Albus
    I know.

Scorpius
    I mean, quite spectacular. Humiliate
Cedric to save Cedric. Clever. And Rose?

Albus
    That I'm saving as a sparkly surprise.
I **can** do it without you – but I **want**
you there. Because I want us to do this
together. Set things right together.
So . . . will you come?

Scorpius
    But, just a minute, isn't – wasn't –
the second task took place in the lake
and you're not allowed to leave the
school building?

Albus grins.

Albus
    Yes. About that . . . we need to find
the girls' bathroom on the first floor.

Act Two

Scene Seventeen

Hogwarts, Staircases

Ron is walking down the staircase, consumed, and then he sees Hermione and his expression changes entirely.

Ron
Professor Granger.

Hermione looks across, her heart leaps a bit too (though she won't admit it).

Hermione
Ron. What are you doing here?

Ron

Panju got in a little trouble in Potions class. Was showing off of course and put the wrong thing with the wrong thing, and now he has no eyebrows and a rather large moustache, apparently. Which doesn't suit him. I didn't want to come but Padma says that when it comes to facial growths, sons need their fathers. Have you done something with your hair?

Hermione

Just combed it I suspect.

Ron

Well . . . combing it suits you.

Hermione looks at Ron slightly strangely.

Hermione

Ron, will you stop looking at me like that?

Ron **(summoning confidence)**

You know, Harry's boy Albus – said to me the other day that he thought you and I were – married. Ha ha. Ha. Ha. Ridiculous, I know.

Hermione
    Very ridiculous.

Ron
    He even thought we had a daughter.
That'd be strange wouldn't it?

**The two lock eyes. Hermione is
the first to break away.**

Hermione
    More than strange.

Ron
    Exactly. We're – friends and that's all.

Hermione
    Absolutely. Only – friends.

Ron
    Only – friends. Funny word – friends.
Not that funny. Just a word really.
Friends. Friend. Funny friend. You, my
funny friend, my Hermione. Not that –
not **my** Hermione, you understand – not
my Hermione – not mine – you know,
but . . .

Hermione
  I know.

  There's a pause. Neither of them moves the smallest inch. Everything feels too important for movement. Then Ron coughs.

Ron
  Well. Must get on. Sort Panju out. Teach him the finer arts of moustache grooming.

  He walks on, he turns, looks at Hermione. She looks back, he hurries on again.

  Your hair really does very much suit you.

———

Act Two

Scene Eighteen

Hogwarts, Headmistress's Office

Professor McGonagall is onstage on her own. She looks at the map. She frowns to herself. She taps it with her wand. She smiles to herself at a good decision made.

Professor McGonagall
Mischief managed.

There's a rattling.

The whole stage seems to vibrate.

Ginny is the first through the fireplace, and then Harry.

Act Two   Scene Eighteen

Ginny
Professor, I can't say that ever gets more dignified.

Professor McGonagall
Potter. You're back. And you seem to have finally ruined my carpet.

Harry
I need to find my son. We need to.

Professor McGonagall
Harry, I've considered this and decided I want no part of it. Whatever you threaten, I—

Harry
Minerva, I come here in peace, not war. I should never have spoken to you that way.

Professor McGonagall
I just don't think I can interfere in friendships and I believe—

Harry
I need to say sorry to you and sorry to Albus, will you give me that chance?

Draco arrives behind them with a bang of soot.

Professor McGonagall
 Draco?

Draco
 He needs to see his son, and I need to see mine.

Harry
 Like I say – peace – not war.

Professor McGonagall studies his face, she sees the sincerity she needs to see. She takes the map back out of her pocket. She opens it up.

Professor McGonagall
 Well, peace is certainly something I can be part of.

She taps it with her wand. Sighs.

 I solemnly swear that I'm up to no good.

The map is lit into action.

Act Two Scene Eighteen

Well, they are together.

Draco
    In the girls' bathroom on the first floor. What on earth would they be doing there?

———————

Act Two
Scene Nineteen

Hogwarts,
Girls' Bathroom

**Scorpius and Albus enter
a bathroom. In the centre of it
is a large Victorian sink.**

Scorpius
 So let me get this right – the plan is Engorgement . . .

Albus
 Yes. Scorpius, that soap if you may . . .

Scorpius fishes a soap out of the sink.

 Engorgio!

Act Two Scene Nineteen

He fires a bolt from his wand across the room. The soap blows up to four times its size.

Scorpius
   Nice. Consider me engorgimpressed.

Albus
   The second task was the lake task. They had to retrieve something which was stolen from them, which turned out to be—

Scorpius
   —people they loved.

Albus
   Cedric used a Bubble-Head Charm to swim through the lake. All we do is follow him in there, and use Engorgement to turn him into something rather larger. We know the Time-Turner doesn't give us long, so we're going to be quick. Get to him and Engorgio his head and watch him float out of the lake – away from the task – away from the competition . . .

Scorpius
But – you still haven't told me how
we're going to actually get to the
lake . . .

**And then suddenly a jet of
water emerges from the sink and
after it ascends a very wet Moaning
Myrtle.**

Moaning Myrtle
Whoah. That feels good. Never used
to enjoy that. But when you get to my
age, you take what you can . . .

Scorpius
Of course – you're a genius –
Moaning Myrtle . . .

**Moaning Myrtle swoops down on
to Scorpius.**

Moaning Myrtle
What did you call me? Do I moan?
Am I moaning now? **Am I? Am I?**

Scorpius
No, I didn't mean . . .

Act Two   Scene Nineteen

Moaning Myrtle
   What's my name?

Scorpius
   Myrtle.

Moaning Myrtle
   Exactly – Myrtle. Myrtle Elizabeth
Warren – a pretty name – my name. No
need for the Moaning.

Scorpius
   Well . . .

Moaning Myrtle (she giggles)
   It's been a while. Boys. In my
bathroom. In my girls' bathroom.
Well, that's not right . . . but then
again, I always did have a soft spot
for the Potters. And I was moderately
partial to a Malfoy too. Now how can I
help you pair?

Albus
   You were there Myrtle – in the lake.
They wrote about you. There must be a
way out of these pipes.

Moaning Myrtle
I've been everywhere. But where specifically were you thinking?

Albus
The second task. The lake task. In the Triwizard Tournament. Twenty-five years ago. Harry and Cedric.

Moaning Myrtle
Such a shame the pretty one had to die. Not that your father is not pretty – but Cedric Diggory – you'd be amazed at how many girls I had to hear doing love incantations in this very bath-room . . . and the weeping after he was taken.

Albus
Help us Myrtle, help us get into that same lake.

Moaning Myrtle
You think I can help you travel in time?

Albus
We need you to keep a secret.

Act Two Scene Nineteen

Moaning Myrtle
I love secrets. I won't tell a soul.
Cross my heart and hope to die. Or –
the equivalent. For ghosts. You know.

**Albus nods at Scorpius, who
reveals the Time-Turner.**

Albus
We can travel in time. You're going to
help us travel the pipes. We're going to
save Cedric Diggory.

Moaning Myrtle **(grins)**
Well, that sounds like fun.

Albus
And we've no time to lose.

Moaning Myrtle
This very sink. This very sink empties
directly into the lake. It breaks every
bylaw but this school has always been
antiquated. Dive in and you will be piped
straight to it.

**Albus pulls himself into the sink,
dumping his cloak as he does.
Scorpius copies.**

Albus hands Scorpius some green foliage in a bag.

Albus
Some for me and some for you.

Scorpius
Gillyweed? We're using Gillyweed? To breathe under water?

Albus
Just like my dad did. Now, are you ready?

Scorpius
Remember, this time, we can't be caught out by the clock . . .

Albus
Five minutes, that's all we allow for, before we get pulled back to the present.

Scorpius
Tell me this is all going to be okay.

Albus **(grinning)**
It's all going to be entirely okay. Are you ready?

Act Two Scene Nineteen

Albus takes the Gillyweed and disappears down.

Scorpius
  No, Albus – Albus –

He looks up, he and Moaning Myrtle are alone.

Moaning Myrtle
  I do like brave boys.

Scorpius **(a little bit scared, a tiny bit brave)**
  Then I'm entirely ready. For whatever comes.

He takes the Gillyweed and disappears down.

Moaning Myrtle is left alone onstage.

There is a giant whoosh of light and smash of noise. And time stops. And then it turns over, thinks a bit, and begins spooling backwards . . .

The boys are gone.

267

Harry appears at a run, a deep frown on his face, behind him Draco, Ginny and Professor McGonagall.

Harry
  Albus . . . Albus . . .

Ginny
  He's gone.

They find the boys' cloaks on the ground.

Professor McGonagall **(consulting the map)**
  He's disappeared. No, he's travelling under Hogwarts grounds, no, he's disappeared—

Draco
  How is he doing this?

Moaning Myrtle
  He's using a rather pretty trinket thingy.

Harry
  Myrtle!

Act Two Scene Nineteen

Moaning Myrtle
Oops, you caught me. And I was trying so hard to hide. Hello, Harry. Hello, Draco. Have you been bad boys again?

Harry
What trinket is he using?

Moaning Myrtle
I think it was a secret, but I could never keep anything from you Harry. How is it you've grown handsomer and handsomer as you've aged? And you're taller.

Harry
My son is in danger. I need your help. What are they doing Myrtle?

Moaning Myrtle
He's after saving a dishy boy. A certain Cedric Diggory.

Harry immediately realises what's happened, and is horrified.

Professor McGonagall
But Cedric Diggory died years ago . . .

Moaning Myrtle
He seemed quite confident he could get around that fact. He's very confident Harry, just like you.

Harry
He heard me talking – to Amos Diggory . . . could he have . . . the Ministry's Time-Turner. No, that's impossible.

Professor McGonagall
The Ministry has a Time-Turner? I thought they were destroyed?

Moaning Myrtle
Isn't everyone so naughty?

Draco
Can someone please explain what's going on?

Harry
Albus and Scorpius are not disappearing and reappearing – they're travelling. Travelling in time.

Act Two
Scene Twenty

Triwizard Tournament, Lake, 1995

Ludo Bagman
    Ladies and gentlemen, boys and girls, I give you – the greatest – the fabulous – the one – and the only Triwizard Tournament! If you're from Hogwarts. Give me a cheer.

There's a loud cheer.

And now Albus and Scorpius are swimming through the lake. Descending through the water with graceful ease.

    If you're from Durmstrang – give me a cheer.

There's a loud cheer.

And if you're from Beauxbatons give me a cheer.

There's a slightly less limp cheer.

The French are getting into this.

And they're off . . . Viktor's a shark, of course he is, Fleur looks remarkable, ever plucky Harry is using Gillyweed, clever Harry, very clever – and Cedric – well, Cedric, what a treat ladies and gentlemen, Cedric is using a Bubble Charm to cruise through the lake.

Cedric Diggory approaches them through the water, a bubble over his head. Albus and Scorpius raise their wands together and fire an Engorgement Charm through the water.

He turns and looks at them confused. And it hits him. And around him the water glows gold.

And then Cedric starts to grow – and grow again – and grow some more.

Act Two   Scene Twenty

He looks around himself – entirely panicked. And the boys watch as Cedric ascends helplessly through the water.

But no, what's this . . . Cedric Diggory is ascending out of the water and seemingly out of the competition. Oh, ladies and gentlemen, we don't have our winner but we certainly have our loser. Cedric Diggory is turning into a balloon and this balloon wants to fly. Fly, ladies and gentlemen, fly. Fly out of the task and out of the tournament and – oh my, it gets wilder still, around Cedric fireworks **explode** declaiming – 'Ron loves Hermione' – and the crowd love that – oh, ladies and gentlemen, the look on Cedric's face. It's quite some picture, it's quite some sight, it's quite some tragedy. This is a humiliation, there's no other word for it.

And Albus smiles widely and high-fives Scorpius in the water.

And Albus points up, and Scorpius nods, and they start to

swim ever upward. And as Cedric ascends people start to laugh, and everything changes.

The world becomes darker. The world becomes almost black in fact.

And there's a flash. And a bang. And the Time-Turner ticks to a stop. And we're back in the present.

Scorpius suddenly emerges, shooting up through the water. And he's triumphant.

Scorpius
Woooo – hoooooo!

He looks around, surprised. Where's Albus? He puts his arms into the air.

We did it!

He waits another beat.

Albus?

Albus still doesn't emerge.

Act Two Scene Twenty

Scorpius treads water, he thinks and then he ducks back into the water.

He emerges back up again. Now thoroughly panicked. He looks around.

Albus . . . Albus . . . Albus.

And there's a whisper in Parseltongue. Which travels fast around the audience. He's coming. He's coming. He's coming.

Dolores Umbridge
Scorpius Malfoy. Get out of the lake. Get out of the lake. Right now.

She pulls him out of the water.

Scorpius
Miss. I need help. Please, Miss.

Dolores Umbridge
Miss? I'm Professor Umbridge, the Headmistress of your school, I'm no Miss.

Scorpius
You're the Headmistress? But I . . .

Part One

Dolores Umbridge

I am the Headmistress and however important your family may be – it doesn't give you an excuse to dilly-dally, to mess about.

Scorpius

There's a boy in this lake. You need to get help. I'm looking for my friend, Miss. Professor. Headmaster. One of Hogwarts's students, Miss. I'm looking for Albus Potter.

Dolores Umbridge

Potter? Albus Potter? There's no such student. In fact, there hasn't been a Potter at Hogwarts for years – and that boy didn't turn out so well. Not so much rest in peace, Harry Potter, more rest in perpetual despair. Total troublemaker.

Scorpius

Harry Potter's dead?

Suddenly from around the auditorium, the feel of a breath of the wind. Some black robes arise around people. Black robes that become black shapes. That become Dementors.

Act Two   Scene Twenty

Flying Dementors through the auditorium. These black deadly shapes, these black deadly forces. They are everything to be feared. And they suck the spirit from the room.

The wind continues. This is Hell. And then right from the back of the room and whispering around everyone. Words said with an unmistakeable voice. The voice of Voldemort . . .

Haaarry Potttter . . .

Harry's dream has come to life.

Dolores Umbridge
Have you swallowed something funny in there? Become a Mudblood without any of us noticing? Harry Potter died over twenty years ago as part of that failed coup on the school – he was one of those Dumbledore terrorists we bravely overthrew at the Battle of Hogwarts. Now come along – I don't know what game you're playing but you're upsetting the Dementors and entirely ruining Voldemort Day.

And the Parseltongue whispers grow louder and louder. Grow monstrously loud. And giant banners with snake symbols upon them descend over the stage.

Scorpius
  Voldemort Day?

We cut to black.

———

End of Part One

Part Two

Part Two
Act Three

Act Three
Scene One

Hogwarts,
Headmistress's Office

Scorpius enters the office of Dolores Umbridge. He is dressed in darker, blacker robes. He has a pensive look on his face. He remains coiled and alert.

Dolores Umbridge
  Scorpius. Thank you so much for coming to see me.

Scorpius
  Headmistress.

Dolores Umbridge
  Scorpius, I've thought for a long time that you have Head Boy potential, as

you know. Pure-blooded, a natural leader, wonderfully athletic . . .

Scorpius
Athletic?

Dolores Umbridge
No need to be modest, Scorpius. I've seen you on the Quidditch pitch, there's rarely a Snitch you don't catch. You are a highly valued student. Valued by the faculty. Valued especially by me. I've positively glowed about you in dispatches to the Augurey. Our work together, flushing out the more dilettante students has made this school a safer – purer – place.

Scorpius
Has it?

There is the sound of a scream from off. Scorpius turns towards it. But he dismisses the thought. He must and he will control himself.

Dolores Umbridge
But in the three days since I found you in that lake on Voldemort Day,

you've become . . . odder and odder –
in particular, this sudden obsession with
Harry Potter . . .

Scorpius
    I don't . . .

Dolores Umbridge
    Questioning everyone you can about
the Battle of Hogwarts. How Potter died.
Why Potter died. And this ludicrous fasci-
nation with Cedric Diggory. Scorpius
– we've checked you for hexes and
curses – there were none we can see –
so I'm asking if there's anything I can do
– to restore you to what you were . . .

Scorpius
    No. No. Consider me restored.
Temporary aberration. That's all.

Dolores Umbridge
    So we can continue our work together?

Scorpius
    We can.

**She puts her hand to her heart,
and touches her wrists together.**

Part Two

Dolores Umbridge
   For Voldemort and Valour.

Scorpius **(trying to copy)**
   For – um – yes.

Act Three
Scene Two

Hogwarts, Grounds

Karl Jenkins
Hey Scorpion King.

Scorpius is high-fived. It's painful, he takes it.

Yann Fredericks
We're still on right, tomorrow night?

Karl Jenkins
Because we are ready to spill some proper Mudblood guts.

Polly Chapman
Scorpius.

Polly Chapman is standing on the stairs, Scorpius turns towards her, surprised to hear her say his name.

Scorpius
  Polly Chapman?

Polly Chapman
  Shall we cut to it? I know everyone is waiting to know who you're going to ask because, you know, you need to ask someone and I've been asked by three people already and I know I'm not alone in refusing them all. In case, you know, you were to ask me.

Scorpius
  Right.

Polly Chapman
  Which would be great. If you were interested. Which rumour is – you are. And I just want to make clear – at this moment – that I am also interested. And that isn't a rumour. That's a – f-a-c-t – fact.

Act Three Scene Two

Scorpius
That's um – great, but – what are we talking about?

Polly Chapman
The Blood Ball of course – who you – the Scorpion King, are taking to the Blood Ball.

Scorpius
You – Polly Chapman – want me to take you to a – ball?

There is the sound of screaming behind him.

What is that screaming?

Polly Chapman
Mudbloods of course. In the dungeons. Your idea wasn't it? What's going on with you? Oh Potter, I've got blood on my shoes again . . .

She bends and carefully cleans the blood off her shoes.

Like the Augurey insists – the future is ours to make – so here I am –

making a future – with you. For
Voldemort and Valour.

Scorpius
For Voldemort it is.

**Polly walks on, Scorpius looks
agonised after her. What is this world
– and what is he within it?**

Act Three
Scene Three

Ministry of Magic, Office of the Head of Magical Law Enforcement

Draco is impressive in a way we haven't seen. He has the smell of power about him. Flying down either side of the room are Augurey flags – with the bird emblazoned in a fascistic manner.

Draco
   You are late.

Scorpius
   This is your office?

Draco
You are late and unapologetic. Maybe
you are determined to compound the
problem.

Scorpius
You're Head of Magical Law
Enforcement?

Draco
How dare you! How dare you
embarrass me and keep me waiting and
then not apologise for it!

Scorpius
Sorry.

Draco
Sir.

Scorpius
Sorry, sir.

Draco
I did not bring you up to be sloppy,
Scorpius. I did not bring you up to
humiliate me at Hogwarts.

Act Three Scene Three

Scorpius
Humiliate you, sir?

Draco
Harry Potter, asking questions about Harry Potter, of all the embarrassing things. How dare you disgrace the Malfoy name.

Scorpius
Oh no. Are you responsible? No. No. You can't be.

Draco
Scorpius . . .

Scorpius
The **Daily Prophet** today – three wizards blowing up bridges to see how many Muggles they can kill with one blast – is that you?

Draco
Be very careful.

Scorpius
The 'Mudblood' death camps, the torture, the burning alive of those that oppose him. How much of that is you?

Mum always told me that you were a better man than I could see, but this is what you really are isn't it? A murderer, a torturer, a—

Draco rises up and pulls Scorpius hard on to the table. The violence is surprising and deadly.

Draco
Do not use her name in vain, Scorpius. Do not score points that way. She deserves better than that.

Scorpius says nothing. Horrified and scared. Draco reads this. He lets go of Scorpius's head. He doesn't like hurting his son.

And no, those idiots blasting Muggles, that's not my doing, though it'll be me the Augurey asks to bribe the Muggle Prime Minister with gold . . . Did your mother really say that of me?

Scorpius
She said that grandfather didn't like her very much – opposed the match – thought she was too Muggle-loving –too

weak – but that you defied him for her. She said it was the bravest thing she'd ever seen.

Draco
She made being brave very easy, your mother.

Scorpius
But that was – another you.

He looks at his dad, who looks back with a frown.

I've done bad things, you've done worse. What have we become, Dad?

Draco
We haven't become anything – we simply are as we are.

Scorpius
The Malfoys. The family you can always rely on to make the world a murkier place.

This hits home with Draco, he looks carefully at Scorpius.

Draco
This business at the school – what's inspired it?

Scorpius
I don't want to be who I am.

Draco
And what's brought that on?

Scorpius desperately thinks for a way of describing his story.

Scorpius
I've seen myself in a different way.

Draco
You know what I loved most about your mother? She could always help me find light in the darkness. She made the world – my world anyway – less – what was the word you used – 'murky'.

Scorpius
Did she?

Draco studies his son.

Act Three   Scene Three

Draco
  There's more of her in there than I thought.

Beat. He looks at Scorpius carefully.

  Whatever you're doing – do it safely. I can't lose you too.

Scorpius
  Yes. Sir.

Draco looks at his son one last time – trying to understand his head.

Draco
  For Voldemort and Valour.

Scorpius looks at him and backs out of the room.

Scorpius
  For Voldemort and Valour.

Act Three

Scene Four

Hogwarts, Library

Scorpius enters the library and starts to desperately look through books. He finds a history book.

Scorpius
    How did Cedric become a Death Eater? What have I missed? Find me some – light in the darkness.

Craig Bowker Jr
    Why are you here?

Scorpius turns to look at a rather desperate-looking Craig, his clothes tattered and worn.

Act Three Scene Four

Scorpius
Why can't I be here?

Craig Bowker Jr
It's not ready yet. I'm working as fast as I can. But Professor Snape sets so much of it, and writing the essay in two different ways. I mean, I'm not complaining . . . sorry.

Scorpius
Start again. From the beginning. What's not ready?

Craig Bowker Jr
Your Potions homework. And I'm happy to do it – grateful even – and I know you hate homework and books, and I never let you down, you know that.

Scorpius
I hate homework?

Craig Bowker Jr
You're the Scorpion King. Of course you hate homework. What are you doing with **A History of Magic**? I could do that assignment too?

Pause. Scorpius looks at Craig a moment and then walks away. Craig exits.

After a moment Scorpius returns with a frown.

Scorpius
Did he say Snape?

———

Act Three
Scene Five

Hogwarts, Potions Classroom

Scorpius runs into the Potions classroom. Slamming back the door. Severus Snape looks up at him.

Snape
    Did no one teach you to knock, boy?

Scorpius looks up at Snape, slightly breathless, slightly unsure, slightly exultant.

Scorpius
    Severus Snape. This is an honour.

Snape
    Professor Snape will do fine. You may

301

behave like a king at this school Malfoy, but that doesn't make us all your subjects.

Scorpius
But you're the answer . . .

Snape
How very pleasant for me. If you've got something to say boy, then please say it . . . if not, close the door on your way out.

Scorpius
I need your help.

Snape
I exist to serve.

Scorpius
I just don't know what help I – need. Are you still undercover now? Are you still working secretly for Dumbledore?

Snape
Dumbledore? Dumbledore's dead. And my work for him was public – I taught in his school.

Act Three　Scene Five

Scorpius

No. That's not all you did. You watched the Death Eaters for him. You advised him. Everyone thought you'd murdered him – but it turned out you'd been supporting him. You saved the world.

Snape

These are very dangerous allegations, boy. And don't think the Malfoy name will prevent me inflicting punishment.

Scorpius

What if I was to tell you there was another world – another world in which Voldemort was defeated at the Battle of Hogwarts, in which Harry Potter and Dumbledore's Army won, how would you feel then . . .

Snape

I'd say that the rumours of Hogwarts's beloved Scorpion King losing his mind are well founded.

Scorpius

There was a stolen Time-Turner. I stole a Time-Turner. With Albus. We tried to bring Cedric Diggory back from the dead, when he was dead. We tried to stop him winning the Triwizard Tournament. But by doing so we turned him into an almost different person entirely.

Snape
   Harry Potter won that Triwizard Tournament.

Scorpius
   He wasn't supposed to do it alone. Cedric was supposed to win it with him. But we humiliated him out of the tournament. And as a result of that humiliation he became a Death Eater. I can't work out what he did in the Battle of Hogwarts – whether he killed someone or – but he did something and it changed everything.

Snape
   Cedric Diggory killed only one wizard and not a significant one – Neville Longbottom.

Scorpius
   Oh, of course, that's it! Professor

Longbottom was supposed to kill Nagini, Voldemort's snake. Nagini had to die before Voldemort could die. That's it! You've solved it! We destroyed Cedric, he killed Neville, Voldemort won the battle. Can you see? Can you see it?

Snape
   I can see this is a Malfoy game. Get out before I alert your father and plunge you into deep trouble.

Scorpius thinks and then plays his final, desperate, card.

Scorpius
   You loved his mother. I don't remember everything. I know you loved his mother. Harry's mother. Lily. I know you spent years undercover. I know without you the war could never have been won. How would I know this if I hadn't seen the other world . . . ?

Snape says nothing, overwhelmed.

   Only Dumbledore knew, am I right? And when you lost him you must have felt so alone. I know you're a good man. Harry Potter told his son you're a great man.

Snape looks at Scorpius, unsure what's going on. Is this a trick? He is quite seriously at a loss.

Snape
Harry Potter is dead.

Scorpius
Not in my world. He said you were the bravest man he'd ever met. He knew, you see – he knew your secret – what you did for Dumbledore. And he admired you for it – greatly. And that's why he named his son – my best friend – after you both. Albus Severus Potter.

Snape is stopped. He is deeply moved.

Please – for Lily, for the world, help me.

Snape thinks and then walks up to Scorpius, taking out his wand as he does. Scorpius steps back, scared. Snape fires his wand at the door.

Act Three   Scene Five

Snape
   Colloportus!

An invisible lock slams into place. Snape opens a hatch at the back of the classroom.

   Well, come on then . . .

Scorpius
   Just a question, but where – exactly – are we going?

Snape
   We've had to move many times. Everywhere we've settled they destroyed. This will take us to a room hidden in the roots of the Whomping Willow.

Scorpius
   Okay, who's we?

Snape
   Oh. You'll see.

Act Three
Scene Six

Campaign Room

Scorpius is pinned to the table by a rather magnificent-looking Hermione. Her clothes faded, her eyes blazing, she is full warrior now and it rather suits her.

Hermione
You make one more move and your brain will be a frog and your arms will be rubber.

Snape
Safe. He's safe. **(Beat.)** You know you never could listen. You were a terrible bore of a student and you're a terrible bore of – whatever you are.

Act Three Scene Six

Hermione

I was an excellent student.

Snape

You were moderate to average. He's on our side!

Scorpius

I am, Hermione.

Hermione looks at Scorpius, still very distrustful.

Hermione

Most people know me as Granger. And I don't believe a word you say, Malfoy.

Scorpius

It's all my fault. My fault. And Albus's.

Hermione

Albus? Albus Dumbledore? What's Albus Dumbledore got to do with this?

Snape

He doesn't mean Dumbledore. You may need to sit down.

Part Two

Ron runs in. His hair spiked. His clothes scruffy. He is slightly less good at the rebel look than Hermione is.

Ron
Snape, a royal visit and – **(he sees Scorpius, and is immediately alarmed)** what's he doing here?

He fumbles out his wand.

I'm armed and – entirely dangerous and seriously advise you—

He realises his wand is around the wrong way and turns it right.

—to be very careful—

Snape
He's safe, Ron.

Ron looks at Hermione, who nods.

Ron
Thank Dumbledore for that.

—⁓—

Act Three
Scene Seven

Campaign Room

Hermione is sitting studying the Time-Turner as Ron tries to digest it all.

Ron
    So you're telling me that the whole of history rests on . . . Neville Longbottom? This is pretty wild.

Hermione
    It's true, Ron.

Ron
    Right. And you're sure because . . .

Hermione
What he knows about Snape – about all of us – there's no way he could . . .

Ron
Maybe he's a really good guesser?

Scorpius
I'm not. Can you help?

Ron
We're the only ones that can. Dumbledore's Army has shrunk consider-ably since its peak, in fact, we're pretty much all that's left, but we've kept fighting on. Hiding in plain sight. Doing our best to tickle their nose hairs. Granger here is a wanted woman. I'm a wanted man.

Snape (dryly)
Less-wanted.

Hermione
To be clear: in this other world . . . before you meddled?

Scorpius
Voldemort is dead. Killed in the Battle

of Hogwarts. Harry is Head of Magical Law Enforcement. You're Minister for Magic.

Hermione stops, surprised by this, she looks up with a smile.

Hermione
   I'm Minister for Magic?

Ron **(wanting to join the fun)**
   Brilliant. What do I do?

Scorpius
   You run Weasleys' Wizard Wheezes.

Ron
   Okay, so, she's Minister for Magic and I run a – joke shop?

Scorpius looks at Ron's hurt face.

Scorpius
   You're mostly focused on bringing up your kids.

Ron
   Great. I expect their mother is hot.

Part Two

Scorpius **(blushing)**
Well . . . um . . . depends what you think of . . . the thing is, you two, sort of have kids – together. A daughter and a son.

The two look up, astonished.

Married. In love. Everything. You were shocked the other time too. When you were Defence Against the Dark Arts teacher and Ron was married to Padma. You're **constantly** surprised by it.

Hermione and Ron both look at each other and then look away. And then Ron looks back. Ron clears his throat repeatedly. With less conviction each time.

Hermione
Close your mouth when you're looking at me, Weasley.

Ron does so. Though he remains discombobulated.

And – Snape? What does Snape do in this other world?

Snape
    I'm dead, presumably.

He looks at Scorpius. Scorpius's face drops, Snape smiles thinly.

    You were a little too surprised to see me. How?

Scorpius
    Bravely.

Snape
    Who?

Scorpius
    Voldemort.

Snape
    How very irritating.

There's a silence as Snape digests this.

    Still, there's glory in being taken down by the Dark Lord himself, I suppose.

Hermione
    I'm sorry, Severus.

315

Snape looks at her, and then swallows the pain. He indicates Ron with a flick of his head.

Snape
   Well, at least I'm not married to him.

Hermione
   Which spells did you use?

Scorpius
   Expelliarmus in the first task and Engorgio in the second.

Ron
   Simple Shield Charms should set both of those right.

Snape
   And then you left?

Scorpius
   The Time-Turner took us back, yes. That's the thing – this Time-Turner, you only get five minutes in the past.

Hermione
   And can you still only move in time not space?

Scorpius
Yes, yes, it's – uh – you travel back in the same spot you stand in—

Hermione
Interesting.

Snape and Hermione both know what this means.

Snape
Then it's just me and the boy.

Hermione
No offence, Snape, but I'm not trusting this to anyone . . . it's too important.

Snape
Hermione, you're the most wanted rebel in the wizarding world. Doing this will require you to go outside. When was the last time you were outside?

Hermione
Not for a long time but—

Snape
If you're found outside, the

Dementors will kiss you – they'll suck
out your soul . . .

Hermione
    Severus, I'm done with living off
scraps, making failed attempts at coups,
this is our chance to reset the world.

**She nods at Ron, who pulls down a
map.**

    The first task of the tournament took
place at the edge of the Forbidden
Forest. We turn time here, get to the
tournament – block the spell and then
return safely. With precision – it can be
done and it won't require us to show our
faces outside in our time at all. Then
we'll turn time again, make our way to
the lake, and reverse the second task.

Snape
    You're risking everything—

Hermione
    We get this right, Harry's alive,
Voldemort's dead and the Augurey is
gone. For that no risk is too great.
Though I am sorry what it will cost you.

Snape
    Sometimes costs are made to be borne.

The two look at each other, Snape nods, Hermione nods back, Snape's face crumbles slightly.

I didn't just quote Dumbledore, did I?

Hermione **(with a smile)**
    No, I'm pretty sure that's pure Severus Snape.

She turns to Scorpius, she indicates the Time-Turner.

Malfoy.

Scorpius brings her the Time-Turner. She smiles at it, excited to use a Time-Turner again, excited to use it for this.

Let's hope this works.

She takes the Time-Turner, it begins to vibrate, and then it explodes into a storm of movement.

Part Two

And there is a giant whoosh of light. A smash of noise.

And time stops. And then it turns over, thinks a bit, and begins spooling backwards, slow at first . . .

There is a bang and a flash, and our gang disappears.

———

Act Three
Scene Eight

Edge of the Forbidden Forest, 1994

And we watch our scene from Part One replayed, but at the back of the stage rather than the front. We pick out Albus and Scorpius in their Durmstrang robes. And through it all we hear the 'brilliant' (his words again) Ludo Bagman.

Scorpius, Hermione, Ron and Snape watch out anxiously.

Ludo Bagman
  And Cedric Diggory has entered the stage. And he seems ready. Scared but ready. He dodges this way. He dodges that. The girls swoon as he dives for cover. They cry as one: don't damage

our Diggory, Mr Dragon. And Cedric skirts left and he dives right – and he readies his wand—

Snape
    This is taking too long. The Time-Turner is spinning.

Ludo Bagman
    What has this young, brave, handsome man got up his sleevies now?

As Albus attempts to summon Cedric's wand, Hermione blocks his spell. He looks at his wand, disconsolate, unsure why it hasn't worked.

And then the Time-Turner spins and they look at it and panic as they're pulled into it.

    A dog – he's transfigured a stone into a dog – dog diggity Cedric Diggory – you are a doggy dynamo.

Act Three
Scene Nine

Edge of the Forbidden Forest

They are returned from time, at the edge of the forest, and Ron is in a lot of pain. Snape looks around, immediately aware of the mess they're in.

Ron
Ow. Ow. Owwwwwww.

Hermione
Ron . . . Ron . . . what has it done to you?

Snape
Oh no, I knew it.

Scorpius
   ~~The Time-Turner~~ did something to Albus too. The first time we went back.

Ron
   Useful – time to – ow – tell us.

Snape
   We're above ground. We need to move. Now.

Hermione
   Ron, you can still walk, come on . . .

Ron does stand up, shouting in pain. Snape raises his wand.

Scorpius
   Did it work?

Hermione
   We blocked the spell. Cedric kept his wand. Yes. It worked.

Snape
   But we came back to the wrong place – we are outside. You are outside.

Act Three Scene Nine

Ron
    We need to use the Time-Turner
again – get out of here—

Snape
    We need to find shelter. We're
horribly exposed.

**Suddenly from around the audito-
rium, the feel of the breath of an icy
wind.**

**Some black robes arise around
people. Black robes that become black
shapes. That become Dementors.**

Hermione
    Too late.

Snape
    This is a disaster.

Hermione **(she realises what she
has to do)**
    They're after me, not any of you.

    Ron. I love you and I always have.
But the three of you need to run. Go.
Now.

Ron
What?

Scorpius
What?

Ron
Can we talk about the love thing first?

Hermione
This is still Voldemort's world. And I am done with it. Reversing the next task will change everything.

Scorpius
But they'll kiss you. They'll suck out your soul.

Hermione
And then you'll change the past. And then they won't. Go. Now.

The Dementors sense them. From all sides screaming shapes descend.

Snape
Go! We go.

Act Three   Scene Nine

**He pulls on Scorpius's arm.
Scorpius reluctantly goes with him.**

Hermione looks at Ron.

Hermione
You're supposed to be going, too.

Ron
Well, they are after me a bit and I really am in quite a lot of pain. And, you know, I'd rather be here. Expecto—

As he reaches up to cast the spell, Hermione stops his arm.

Hermione
Let's keep them here and give the boy the best chance we can.

Ron looks at her and then nods sadly.

Hermione
A daughter.

Ron
And a son. I liked that idea too.

He looks around – he knows his fate.

I'm scared.

Hermione
Kiss me.

Ron thinks and then does. And then the two are yanked apart. And pinned to the ground. And we watch as a golden-whitish haze is pulled from their bodies. They have their souls sucked from them. And it is terrifying.

Scorpius watches – helplessly.

Snape
Let's get down to the water. Walk. Don't run.

Snape looks at Scorpius.

Stay calm, Scorpius. They may be blind but they can sense your fear.

Scorpius looks at Snape.

Act Three Scene Nine

Scorpius
They just sucked out their souls.

A Dementor swoops down low over them and settles in front of Scorpius.

Snape
Think of something else, Scorpius.
Occupy your thoughts.

Scorpius
I feel cold. I can't see. There's a fog inside me – around me.

Snape
You're a king, and I'm a professor.
They'll only attack with good reason.
Think about those you love, think about why you're doing this.

Scorpius
I can hear my mother. She wants me – my – help but she knows I can't – help.

Snape
Listen to me, Scorpius. Think about Albus. You're giving up your kingdom for Albus, right?

Scorpius is helpless. Consumed by all the Dementor is making him feel.

Snape
One person. All it takes is one person. I couldn't save Harry for Lily. So now I give my allegiance to the cause she believed in. And it's possible – that along the way I started believing in it myself.

Scorpius smiles at Snape. He steps decisively away from the Dementor.

Scorpius
The world changes and we change with it. I am better off in this world. But the world is not better. And I don't want that.

Suddenly Dolores Umbridge emerges in front of them.

Dolores Umbridge
Professor Snape!

Snape
Professor Umbridge.

Act Three Scene Nine

Dolores Umbridge
Have you heard the news? We've caught that traitorous Mudblood Hermione Granger. She was just out here.

Snape
That's – fantastic.

Dolores is staring at Snape. He looks back.

Dolores Umbridge
With you. Granger was with you.

Snape
With me? You're mistaken.

Dolores Umbridge
With you and Scorpius Malfoy. A student I'm becoming increasingly concerned about.

Scorpius
Well . . .

Snape
Dolores, we're late for class, so if you'll excuse us . . .

Dolores Umbridge
    If you're late for class, why are you
not heading back to the school? Why are
you heading to the lake?

**There's a moment of pure silence.
And then Snape does something
hugely unusual – he smiles.**

Snape
    How long have you suspected?

**Dolores Umbridge rises off the
ground. She opens her arms wide, full
of Dark Magic. She takes out her wand.**

Dolores Umbridge
    Years. And I should have acted upon
it far earlier.

Snape is faster with his wand.

Snape
    Depulso!

**Dolores is propelled backwards
through the air.**

She always was too grand for her own good. There's no turning back now.

The sky turns even blacker still around them.

Expecto Patronum!

Snape sends forward a Patronus, and it's a beautiful white shape of a doe.

Scorpius
   A doe? Lily's Patronus.

Snape
   Strange isn't it? What comes from within.

Dementors start to appear all around them. Snape knows what this means.

You need to run. I will keep them at bay for as long as I can.

Scorpius
   Thank you for being my light in the darkness.

Snape looks at him, every inch a hero, he softly smiles.

Snape
Tell Albus – tell Albus Severus – I'm proud he carries my name. Now go. Go!

The doe looks back at Scorpius, and then starts to run.

Scorpius thinks and then runs after the doe and around him the world gets scarier. A blood-curdling scream goes up at one side. He sees the lake and throws himself inside.

Snape readies himself.

Snape is pulled hard to the ground and then pushed high into the air as his soul is ripped from him. And the screams just seem to multiply.

The doe turns to him, with beautiful eyes and disappears.

There is a bang and a flash. And then silence. And then there's more silence.

It's so still, it's so peaceful, it's so perfectly tranquil.

And then Scorpius ascends to the surface. Breathing deeply. He looks around himself. Breathing deep, panicked breaths. He looks up at the sky. The sky certainly seems – bluer than before.

And then Albus ascends after him. There's a silence. Scorpius just looks at Albus, disbelieving. Both boys breathe in and out.

Albus
Whoah!

Scorpius
Albus!

Albus
That was close! Did you see that Merman? The guy with the – and then the thing with the – whoah!

Scorpius
It's you!

Albus
It was weird though – I thought I saw Cedric start to expand – but then he sort of started shrinking again – and I looked at you and you had your wand out . . .

Scorpius
You have no idea how good it is to see you again.

Albus
You just saw me two minutes ago.

Scorpius hugs Albus in the water, a difficult task.

Scorpius
A lot has happened since then.

Albus
Careful. You're drowning me. What are you wearing?

Scorpius
What am I wearing? **(He pulls off his cloak.)** What are you wearing? Yes! You're in Slytherin.

Act Three   Scene Nine

Albus
   Did it work? Did we do anything?

Scorpius
   No. And it's brilliant.

Albus looks at him – disbelieving.

Albus
   What? We failed.

Scorpius
   Yes. Yes. And it's amazing.

**He splashes hard in the water.
Albus pulls himself out to the
bank.**

Albus
   Scorpius. Have you been eating too
many sweets again?

Scorpius
   There you go you see – all dry
humour and Albus-y. I love it.

Albus
   Now I'm starting to get worried . . .

Harry enters and sprints to the side of the water. Followed quickly by Draco, Ginny and Professor McGonagall.

Harry
    Albus. Albus. Are you okay?

Scorpius **(overjoyed)**
    Harry! It's Harry Potter! And Ginny. And Professor McGonagall. And Dad. My dad. Hi. Dad.

Draco
    Hello, Scorpius.

Albus
    You're all here.

Ginny
    And Myrtle told us everything.

Albus
    What is going on?

Professor McGonagall
    You're the one who's just returned from time. Why don't you tell us?

Act Three Scene Nine

Scorpius immediately registers what they know.

Scorpius
Oh no. Oh bother. Where is it?

Albus
Just returned from where?

Scorpius
I've lost it! I've lost the Time-Turner.

Albus **(looking at Scorpius, deeply annoyed)**
You've lost what?

Harry
Time to cut the pretence, Albus.

Professor McGonagall
I think you've got some explaining to do.

Act Three
Scene Ten

Hogwarts, Headmistress's Office

Draco, Ginny and Harry stand behind a contrite-looking Scorpius and Albus. Professor McGonagall is fuming.

Professor McGonagall
So to be clear – you illegally jumped off the Hogwarts Express, you invaded and stole from the Ministry of Magic, you took it upon yourself to change time, whereupon you disappeared two people—

Albus
I agree it doesn't sound good.

Professor McGonagall
And your response to disappearing

Hugo and Rose Granger-Weasley was to go back in time again – and this time – instead of losing two people you lost a huge number of people and killed your father – and in doing so you resurrected the worst wizard the world has ever known and heralded in a new age of Dark Magic. **(Dry.)** You're correct, Mr Potter, it doesn't sound good does it? Are you aware how stupid you've been?

Scorpius
    Yes, Professor.

Albus hesitates a moment. He looks at Harry.

Albus
    Yes.

Harry
    Professor, if I may—

Professor McGonagall
    You may not. What you choose to do as parents is your matter, but this is my school, and these are my students, and I will choose what punishment they will face.

Draco
    Seems fair.

Harry looks at Ginny, who shakes her head.

Professor McGonagall
    I should expel you but **(with a look to Harry)** all things considered – I think it might be safer for you to remain in my care. You are in detention for – well, you can consider yourself in detention for the rest of the year. Christmas is cancelled for you. You can forget visiting Hogsmeade ever again. And that's just the start . . .

Suddenly Hermione bursts in. All action and resolve.

Hermione
    What did I miss?

Professor McGonagall **(fierce)**
    It is considered polite to knock when entering a room, Hermione Granger, maybe you missed that.

Hermione **(realises she's over-stepped)**
    Ah.

Professor McGonagall
    If I could also give a detention to you, Minister, I would. Keeping hold of a Time-Turner, of all the stupid things!

Hermione
    In my defence—

Professor McGonagall
    And in a bookcase. You kept it in a bookcase. It's almost laughable.

Hermione
    Minerva. **(There is an intake of breath.)** Professor McGonagall—

Professor McGonagall
    Your children didn't exist!

Hermione has no reply to that.

This happened in my school, under my watch. After all that Dumbledore did, I couldn't live with myself . . .

Hermione

~~I know.~~

Professor McGonagall composes herself for a moment.

Professor McGonagall **(to Albus and Scorpius)**

Your intentions to save Cedric were honourable if misguided. And it does sound as if you were brave, Scorpius, and you, Albus, but the lesson even your father sometimes failed to heed is that bravery doesn't forgive stupidity. Always think. Think what's possible. A world controlled by Voldemort is—

Scorpius

A horrific world.

Professor McGonagall

You are so young. **(She looks at Harry, Draco, Ginny and Hermione.)** You're all so young. You have no idea how dark the wizarding wars got. You were – reckless – with the world some people – some very dear friends of mine and yours – sacrificed a huge amount to create and sustain.

Act Three   Scene Ten

Albus
Yes, Professor.

Scorpius
Yes, Professor.

Professor McGonagall
Go on. Get out. The lot of you. And find me that Time-Turner.

———

Act Three
Scene Eleven

Hogwarts, Slytherin Dormitory

Albus is sitting in his room. Harry enters and looks at his son, full of anger, but cautious to not let it spill.

Harry
Thanks for letting me come up.

Albus turns, he nods at his dad. He's being cautious too.

No luck, as yet, with the Time-Turner searching. They're negotiating with the Merpeople to dredge the lake.

He sits down, uncomfortably.

This is a nice room.

Act Three Scene Eleven

Albus

Green is a soothing colour isn't it? I mean Gryffindor rooms are all well and good, but the trouble with red is – it is said to send you a little mad – not that I'm casting aspersions . . .

Harry

Can you explain why you tried to do this?

Albus

I thought I could – change things – I thought Cedric – it's unfair.

Harry

Of course it's unfair Albus, don't you think I know that? I was there. I saw him die. But to do this . . . to risk all this . . .

Albus

I know.

Harry (failing to contain his anger)

If you were trying to do as I did, you went the wrong way about it. I didn't volunteer for adventure, I was forced into it. You did something really reckless – something really stupid and dangerous – something that could have destroyed everything—

Albus
    I know. Okay, I know.

Pause. Albus wipes away a tear, Harry notices it and takes a breath. He pulls himself back from the brink.

Harry
    Well, I was wrong too – to think Scorpius was Voldemort's son. He wasn't a black cloud.

Albus
    No.

Harry
    And I've locked away the map. You won't see it again. Your mum left your room exactly as it was when you ran away – you know that? Wouldn't let me go in – wouldn't let anyone go in – you really scared her . . . and me.

Albus
    Really scared you?

Act Three Scene Eleven

Harry
   Yes.

Albus
   I thought Harry Potter wasn't afraid of anything?

Harry
   Is that how I make you feel?

Albus looks at his dad, trying to figure him out.

Albus
   I don't think Scorpius said, but when we returned after failing to fix the first task, I was suddenly in Gryffindor house, nothing was better between us then either – so the fact that I'm in Slytherin – that's not the reason for our problems. It's not just about that.

Harry
   No. I know. It's not just about that.

Harry looks at Albus.

Are you okay, Albus?

Part Two

Albus
　　No.

Harry
　　No. Nor me.

—————

Act Three
Scene Twelve

Dream, Godric's Hollow, Graveyard

Young Harry stands looking at a gravestone covered in bunches of flowers. He has a small bunch of flowers in his hand.

Aunt Petunia

Go on then, lay down your grotty little flowers and then let's go. I already hate this poxy little village, I don't know why I even had the thought – Godric's Hollow, Godless Hollow more like, the place is clearly a hive of filth – go on, chop chop.

Young Harry approaches the grave. He stands a moment more.

Part Two

Now, Harry . . . I don't have time for this. Duddy has his Cubs tonight and you know he hates to be late.

Young Harry
Aunt Petunia. We're their last living relatives, right?

Aunt Petunia
Yes. You and I. Yes.

Young Harry
And – they weren't popular? You said they didn't have any friends?

Aunt Petunia
Lily tried – bless her – she tried – it wasn't her fault, but she repelled people – by her very nature. It was her intensity, it was her – manner, it was her – way. And your father – obnoxious man – extraordinarily obnoxious. No friends. Neither of them.

Young Harry
So my question is – why are there so many flowers? Why are there flowers all over their grave?

Act Three   Scene Twelve

Aunt Petunia looks around, she sees all the flowers as if for the first time and it moves her hugely. She approaches and then sits by her sister's grave, trying hard to fight the emotions as they come to her but succumbing all the same.

Aunt Petunia
   Oh. Yes. Well, I suppose there are a – few. Must have blown over from the other graves. Or someone's playing a trick. Yes, I think that's most likely, some young rapscallion with too much time on his hands, has gone around collecting flowers from all the other graves and deposited them here—

Young Harry
   But they're all marked with their names . . . Lily and James, what you did, we will never forget . . . Lily and James, your sacrifice—

Voldemort
   I smell guilt, there is a stench of guilt upon the air.

Part Two

Aunt Petunia (to Young Harry)
Get away. Get away from there.

She pulls him back. Voldemort's hand rises into the air above the Potters' gravestone, the rest of him rises after. We don't see his face but his body provides a jagged, horrific shape.

I knew it. This place is dangerous. The sooner we leave Godric's Hollow the better.

Young Harry is pulled from the stage, but turns to face Voldemort.

Voldemort
Do you still see with my eyes, Harry Potter?

Young Harry exits disturbed as Albus bursts from within Voldemort's cloak. He reaches out a desperate hand towards his dad.

Albus
Dad . . . Dad . . .

Act Three   Scene Twelve

There's some words spoken in Parseltongue.

He's coming. He's coming. He's coming.

And then a scream.

And then right from the back of the room and whispering around everyone. Words said with an unmistakeable voice. The voice of Voldemort . . .

Haaarry Pottttter . . .

Act Three
Scene Thirteen

Harry and Ginny Potter's House, Kitchen

Harry is in a horrible state. Petrified by what he thinks his dreams are telling him.

Ginny
    Harry? Harry? What is it? You were screaming . . .

Harry
    They haven't stopped. The dreams.

Ginny
    They weren't likely to stop immediately. It's been a stressful time and—

Act Three Scene Thirteen

Harry
 But I was never in Godric's Hollow with Petunia. This doesn't—

Ginny
 Harry, you're really scaring me.

Harry
 He's still here, Ginny.

Ginny
 Who's still here?

Harry
 Voldemort. I saw Voldemort and Albus.

Ginny
 And Albus . . . ?

Harry
 He said – Voldemort said – 'I smell guilt, there is a stench of guilt upon the air.' He was talking to me.

Harry looks at her. He touches his scar. Her face falls.

Ginny
 Harry, is Albus still in danger?

Part Two

Harry's face grows white.

Harry
    I think we all are.

Act Three
Scene Fourteen

Hogwarts, Slytherin Dormitory

Scorpius leans ominously over Albus's bedhead.

Scorpius
Albus . . . Psst . . . Albus.

Albus doesn't wake.

Albus!

**Albus wakes with a shock.
Scorpius laughs.**

Albus
Pleasant. That's a pleasant and not scary way to wake up.

Part Two

Scorpius

You know it's the strangest of things but ever since being in the scariest place imaginable I'm pretty much good with fear. I am – Scorpius the Dreadless. I am – Malfoy the Unanxious.

Albus

Good.

Scorpius

I mean, normally, being in lockdown, being in constant detention. It'd break me but now – what's the worst they can do? Bring back Mouldy Voldy and have him torture me? Nope.

Albus

You're scary when you're in a good mood, you know that?

Scorpius

When Rose came up to me today in Potions and called me Bread Head, I almost hugged her. No, there's no almost about it, I actually tried to hug her, and then she kicked me in the shin.

Act Three Scene Fourteen

Albus

I'm not sure being fearless is going to be good for your health.

Scorpius looks at Albus; his face grows more contemplative.

Scorpius

You don't know how good it is to be back here, Albus. I hated it there.

Albus

Apart from the Polly Chapman fancying you bits.

Scorpius

Cedric was a different person entirely – dark, dangerous. My dad – doing anything they wanted him to. And me? I discovered another Scorpius you know? Entitled, angry, mean – people were frightened of me. It feels like we were all tested and we all – failed.

Albus

But you changed things. You had a chance and you changed time back. Changed yourself back.

Scorpius
Only because I knew what I should
be.

Albus digests this.

Albus
Do you think I've been tested too? I
have, haven't I?

Scorpius
No. Not yet.

Albus
You're wrong. The stupid thing wasn't
going back once – anyone can make
that mistake – the stupid thing was
being arrogant enough to go back twice.

Scorpius
We both went back, Albus.

Albus
And why was I so determined to do
this? Cedric? Really? No. I had something to prove. My dad's right – he didn't
volunteer for adventure – me, this, it's
all my fault – and if it wasn't for you
everything could have gone Dark.

Scorpius
But it didn't. And you're to thank for that as much as me. When the Dementors were – inside my head – Severus Snape told me to think of you. You may not have been there Albus, but you were fighting – fighting alongside me.

Albus nods. Touched by this.

And saving Cedric – that wasn't such a bad idea – not in my head anyway – though, you know right – that we definitely can't try again.

Albus
Yes. I do. I do know that.

Scorpius
Good. Then you can help me destroy this.

Scorpius reveals the Time-Turner to Albus.

Albus
I'm pretty sure you told everyone that was on the bottom of a lake.

Scorpius
Turns out Malfoy the Unanxious is a pretty good liar.

Albus
Scorpius, we should tell someone about this . . .

Scorpius
Who? The Ministry kept it before, do you really trust them not to keep it again? Only you and I have experienced how dangerous this is, that means you and I have to destroy it. No one can do what we did Albus. No one. No, **(slightly grandly)** it's time that time-turning became a thing of the past.

Albus
You're quite proud of that phrase, aren't you?

Scorpius
Been working on it all day.

Act Three
Scene Fifteen

Hogwarts,
Slytherin Dormitory

Harry and Ginny move quickly through the dormitory. Craig Bowker Jr trails after them.

Craig Bowker Jr
Can I repeat again? This is against the rules and it's the middle of the night.

Harry
I need to find my son.

Craig Bowker Jr
I know who you are, Mr Potter, but even you must understand that it's against school covenant for parents or professors to enter a house quarters without express permission from . . .

365

Part Two

**Professor McGonagall charges
in behind them.**

Professor McGonagall
  Please don't be tiresome, Craig.

Harry
  You got our message? Good.

Craig Bowker Jr **(shocked)**
  Headmistress. I'm – I was just—

Harry pulls open a bed curtain.

Professor McGonagall
  He's gone?

Harry
  Yes.

Professor McGonagall
  And young Malfoy?

Ginny pulls open another.

Ginny
  Oh no.

Professor McGonagall
Then let's turn this school upside down. Craig, we've work to do . . .

Ginny and Harry stay looking at the bed.

Ginny
Haven't we been here before?

Harry
Something feels even worse this time.

Ginny looks at her husband, full of fear.

Ginny
You spoke to him earlier?

Harry
Yes.

Ginny
You came to his dorm and talked to him?

Harry
You know I did.

Part Two

Ginny

What did you say to our son, Harry?

Harry can hear the accusation in her voice.

Harry

I tried to be honest like you said – I didn't say anything.

Ginny

And you controlled yourself? How heated did it get?

Harry

. . . I don't think I . . . you think I've scared him away again?

Ginny

I can forgive you for one mistake Harry, maybe even two, but the more mistakes you make, the harder to forgive you it becomes.

Act Three
Scene Sixteen

Hogwarts, Owlery

**Scorpius and Albus emerge on
to a roof bathed in silver light.
There's soft hooting all
around them.**

Scorpius
    So, I think a simple Confringo.

Albus
    Definitely not. For something like this
you need Expulso.

Scorpius
    Expulso? Expulso and we'll be
clearing bits of Time-Turner from this
owlery for days.

Part Two

Albus
    Bombarda?

Scorpius
    And wake up everyone in Hogwarts?
Maybe Stupefy. They were originally
destroyed using Stupefy . . .

Albus
    Exactly, it's been done before – let's
do something new, something fun.

Scorpius
    Fun? Look, many wizards overlook the
importance of choosing the right spell but
this really matters. I think it's a much-
underestimated part of modern witchcraft.

Delphi
    'A much-underestimated part of
modern witchcraft' – you two are the
greatest, you know that?

**Scorpius looks up, surprised to
see Delphi has emerged behind them.**

Scorpius
    Wow. You're . . . um . . . what are
you doing here?

Albus
    It felt important to send an owl – let
her know what we're doing – you know?

**Scorpius looks at his friend
accusingly.**

This concerns her too.

**Scorpius thinks, and then nods,
accepting this.**

Delphi
    What concerns me? What's this about?

Albus gets out the Time-Turner.

Albus
    We need to destroy the Time-Turner.
The things Scorpius saw after the second
task . . . I'm so sorry. We can't risk
going back again. We can't save your
cousin.

**Delphi looks at it and then at
them both.**

Delphi
    Your owl said so little . . .

Albus
Imagine the worst possible world, and then double it. People being tortured – Dementors everywhere – a despotic Voldemort – my dad dead, me never born, the world surrounded by Dark Magic. We just – we can't allow that to happen.

Delphi hesitates. And then her face breaks.

Delphi
Voldemort ruled? He was alive?

Scorpius
He ruled everything. It was terrible.

Delphi
Because of what we did?

Scorpius
Humiliating Cedric turned him into a very angry young man and then he became a Death Eater and – and – it all went wrong. Really wrong.

Delphi looks at Scorpius's face carefully. Her face sinks.

Act Three Scene Sixteen

Delphi
A Death Eater?

Scorpius
And a murderer. He killed Professor Longbottom.

Delphi
Then – of course – we need to destroy it.

Albus
You understand?

Delphi
I'll go further than that – I'll say Cedric would have understood. We'll destroy it together, and then we'll go to my uncle. Explain the situation.

Albus
Thank you.

Delphi smiles at them sadly, and then takes the Time-Turner. She looks at it and her expression changes slightly.

Oh, nice mark.

Delphi
    What?

**Delphi's cloak has loosened. An
Augurey tattoo is visible on the back
of her neck.**

Albus
    On your back. I hadn't noticed it
before. The wings. Is that what the
Muggles call a tattoo?

Delphi
    Oh. Yes. Well, it's an Augurey.

Scorpius
    An Augurey?

Delphi
    Haven't you met them in Care of
Magical Creatures? They're sinis-
ter-looking black birds that cry when
rain's coming. Wizards used to believe
that the Augurey's cry foretold death.
When I was growing up, my guardian
kept one in a cage.

Scorpius
    Your . . . guardian?

Delphi looks at Scorpius. Now she has the Time-Turner she's enjoying this game.

Delphi
    She used to say it was crying because it could see I was going to come to a sticky end. She didn't like me much. Euphemia Rowle . . . she only took me in for the gold.

Albus
    Why would you want a tattoo of her bird, then?

Delphi
    It reminds me that the future is mine to make.

Albus
    Cool. I might get an Augurey tattoo.

Scorpius
    The Rowles were pretty extreme Death Eaters.

A thousand thoughts whir inside Scorpius's head.

Part Two

Albus
Come on, let's get destroying . . . Confringo? Stupefy? Bombarda? Which would you use?

Scorpius
Give it back. Give us back the Time-Turner.

Delphi
What?

Albus
Scorpius? What are you doing?

Scorpius
I don't believe you ever were ill. Why didn't you come to Hogwarts? Why are you here now?

Delphi
I'm trying to bring my cousin back!

Scorpius
They called you the Augurey. In – the other world – they called you the Augurey.

A slow smile grows on Delphi's face.

Act Three   Scene Sixteen

Delphi
    The Augurey? I rather like that.

Albus
    Delphi?

She's too quick. Levelling her wand, she repels Scorpius. And she is far stronger – Scorpius tries to keep her back, but she quickly over-powers him.

Delphi
    Fulgari!

Scorpius's arms are bound in vicious, luminous cords.

Scorpius
    Albus. Run.

Albus looks around, bewildered. And then starts to run.

Delphi
    Fulgari!

Albus is propelled to the floor, his hands tied by the same brutal binding.

And that is the first spell I've had to use on you. I thought I'd have to use plenty more. But you're far easier to control than Amos – children, particularly male children, are so naturally pliant aren't they? Now, let's sort this mess out once and for all . . .

Albus
But why? But what? But who are you?

Delphi
Albus. I am the new past.

She pulls Albus's wand from him and snaps it.

I am the new future.

She pulls Scorpius's wand from him and snaps it.

I am the answer this world has been looking for.

Act Three

Scene Seventeen

Ministry of Magic, Hermione's Office

Ron is sitting on Hermione's desk, eating porridge.

Ron

   I can't get over it really. The fact that in some realities we aren't even, you know, married.

Hermione

   Ron whatever this is – I've got ten minutes until the goblins show up to talk security at Gringotts—

Ron

   I mean, we've been together so long – and married for so long – I mean, **so** long—

Part Two

Hermione

If this is your way of saying you want a marital break Ron, then, to be clear, I will skewer you with this quill.

Ron

Shut up. Will you shut up for once? I want to do one of those marriage renewal things I've read about. Marriage renewal. What do you think?

Hermione **(melting slightly)**

You want to marry me again?

Ron

Well, we were only young when we did it the first time and I got very drunk and – well, to be honest, I can't remember much of it and . . . the truth is – I love you Hermione Granger – and whatever time says – I'd like the opportunity to say so in front of lots of other people. Again. Sober.

She looks at him, she smiles, she pulls him to her, she kisses him.

Hermione

You're sweet.

Act Three Scene Seventeen

Ron
And you taste of toffee.

**Hermione laughs. Harry, Ginny
and Draco walk in on them as they
move to kiss again. They spring apart.**

Hermione
Harry, Ginny and – I, uh – Draco –
how lovely to see you—

Harry
The dreams. They've started again,
well, they haven't stopped.

Ginny
And Albus is missing. Again.

Draco
Scorpius too. We've had McGonagall
check the entire school. They're gone.

Hermione
I'll get the Aurors summoned immediately, I'll—

Ron
No, you won't, it's all fine. Albus, I
saw him last night. It's all good.

Part Two

Draco
    Where?

**They all turn to look at Ron, he's
briefly disconcerted but batters on.**

Ron
    I was having a couple of Firewhiskies
with Neville in Hogsmeade – as you do
– setting the world to rights – as we do
– and we were coming back – quite
late, very late, and trying to work out
which Floo I could use because when
you've had a drink sometimes you don't
want to use the tight ones – or the
turny ones or—

Ginny
    Ron, if you could get to the point
before we all strangle you?

Ron
    He hasn't run away – he's having a
quiet moment – he's got himself an
older girlfriend—

Harry
    An older girlfriend?

Ron
    And a cracking one at that – gorgeous silver hair. Saw them on the roof together, near the owlery with Scorpius playing the gooseberry. Nice to see my love potion being used well, I thought.

Harry has a thought.

Harry
    Her hair – was it silver and blue?

Ron
    That's it – silver, blue – yup.

Harry
    He's talking about Delphi Diggory. Niece of – Amos Diggory.

Ginny
    This is about Cedric again?

Harry says nothing, thinking fast. Hermione looks around the room, concerned, and then shouts out of the door.

Hermione
    Ethel. Cancel the goblins.

Act Three
Scene Eighteen

St Oswald's Home for Old Witches and Wizards, Amos's Room

Harry walks in, wand outstretched, with Draco.

Harry
Where are they?

Amos
Harry Potter, and what can I do for you sir? And Draco Malfoy. I am blessed.

Harry
I know how you've used my son.

Amos
I've used your son? No. You sir – you used my beautiful son.

Act Three Scene Eighteen

Draco
Tell us – now – where are Albus and Scorpius or face the profoundest consequences.

Amos
But why would I know where they are?

Draco
Don't play the senility card with us, old man. We know you've been sending him owls.

Amos
I've done nothing of the kind.

Harry
Amos, you're not too old for Azkaban. They were last seen on the Hogwarts tower with your niece when they disappeared.

Amos
I have no idea what you are . . . **(He stops, a beat, confused.)** My niece?

Harry
There are no depths to which you

won't sink are there – yes, your niece, are you denying she was there under your express instructions . . .

Amos
    Yes, I am – I don't have a niece.

This stops Harry.

Draco
    Yes, you do, a nurse, works here. Your niece . . . Delphini Diggory.

Amos
    I know I don't have a niece because I never had any brothers and sisters. And nor did my wife.

Draco
    We need to find out who she is – **now**.

———

Act Three

Scene Nineteen

Hogwarts, Quidditch Pitch

We open on Delphi, enjoying every second of her changed identity. Where there was discomfort and insecurity, now there's just power.

Albus
　　What are we doing on the Quidditch pitch?

Delphi says nothing.

Scorpius
　　The Triwizard Tournament. The third task. The maze. This is where the maze was. We're going back for Cedric.

Part Two

Delphi
Yes, it is time to spare the spare once and for all. We will go back for Cedric and in doing so we will resurrect the world you saw Scorpius . . .

Scorpius
Hell. You want to resurrect hell?

Delphi
I want a return to pure and strong magic. I want to rebirth the Dark.

Scorpius
You want Voldemort's return?

Delphi
The one true ruler of the wizarding world. He will return. Now you've ensured the first two tasks are a little clogged up with magic – there are at least two visits from the future in both of them and I will not risk being revealed or distracted. The third task is clean, so let's start there, shall we?

Albus
We won't stop him – whatever you

force us to do – we know he needs to win the tournament with my dad.

Delphi
I don't just want you to stop him. I want you to humiliate him. He needs to fly out of that maze naked on a broom-stick made of purple feather dusters. Humiliation got you there before and it'll get us there again. And the prophecy will be fulfilled.

Scorpius
Wasn't aware that there was a prophecy – what prophecy?

Delphi
You have seen the world as it should be Scorpius, and today we're going to ensure its return.

Albus
We won't. We won't obey you. Whoever you are. Whatever you want us to do.

Delphi
Of course you will.

Albus
　　You'll have to use Imperio. You'll have to control me.

Delphi
　　No. To fulfil the prophecy, this has to be you, not a puppet of you . . . you have to be the one to humiliate Cedric, so Imperio just won't do – I'll have to force you by other means.

She takes out her wand. She points it at Albus, who sticks his chin out.

Albus
　　Do your worst.

Delphi looks at him. And then turns her wand on Scorpius.

Delphi
　　I will.

Albus
　　No!

Delphi
　　Yes, as I thought – this seems to frighten you more.

390

Act Three   Scene Nineteen

Scorpius
Albus, whatever she does to me – we
can't let her—

Delphi
Crucio!

Scorpius yells out in pain.

Albus
I will . . .

Delphi **(laughing)**
What? What on earth do you think
you can do? A wizardwide disappointment? A sore on your family name?
A spare? You want to stop me hurting
your only friend? Then do what you're
told.

**She looks at Albus. His eyes stay
resistant.**

No? Crucio!

Albus
Stop! Please.

Craig runs in, full of energy.

Craig Bowker Jr
Scorpius? Albus? Everyone's looking for you—

Albus
Craig! Get away. Get help!

Craig Bowker Jr
What's happening?

Delphi
Avada Kedavra!

Delphi sends a blast of green light across the stage. Craig is propelled backwards by it – and is immediately killed.

There's a silence. A silence that seems to last for a long time.

Did you not understand? These are not childish games we are playing here. You are useful to me, your friends are not.

Albus and Scorpius look at Craig's body – their minds in hell.

Act Three Scene Nineteen

It took me a long time to discover your weakness, Albus Potter. I thought it was pride, I thought it was the need to impress your father, but then I realised your weakness was the same as your father's – friendship. You will do exactly as you're told, otherwise Scorpius will die, just like that **spare** did.

She looks at them both.

Voldemort will return and the Augurey will sit at his side. Just as it was prophesied. 'When spares are spared, when time is turned, when unseen children murder their fathers: then will the Dark Lord return.'

She smiles. She pulls Scorpius viciously towards her.

Cedric is the spare, and Albus—

She pulls Albus viciously towards her.

—the unseen child who will kill his father by rewriting time and so return the Dark Lord.

The Time-Turner starts rotating.
She pulls their hands to it.

Now!

And there is a giant whoosh of
light. A smash of noise.

And time stops. And then it turns
over, thinks a bit, and begins spooling
backwards, slow at first . . .

And then it speeds up.

And then there's a sucking noise.
And a bang.

Act Three
Scene Twenty

Triwizard Tournament, Maze, 1995

The maze is a spiral of hedges that don't stop moving. Delphi walks determinedly through it. Behind her she drags Albus and Scorpius. Their arms bound, their legs reluctantly moving.

Ludo Bagman
    Ladies and gentlemen, boys and girls, I give you – the greatest – the fabulous – the one – and the only Triwizard Tournament!

    There's a loud cheer. Delphi turns left.

If you're from Hogwarts. Give me a cheer.

There's a loud cheer.

If you're from Durmstrang – give me a cheer.

There's a loud cheer.

And if you're from Beauxbatons give me a cheer.

There's a fulsome cheer.

Delphi and the boys are forced to move as a hedge closes upon them.

The French finally showing us what they're capable of there. Ladies and gentlemen, I give you – the final of the Triwizard tasks. A maze of mysteries, a disease of uncontrollable darkness, for this maze – it lives. It lives.

Viktor Krum passes across the stage, moving through the maze.

And why risk this living nightmare?

Because inside this maze is a Cup –
and not just any Cup – yes, the
Triwizard trophy stands within this
vegetation.

Delphi
    Where is he? Where is Cedric?

**A hedge almost dissects Albus and
Scorpius.**

Scorpius
    The hedges want to kill us too? This
gets better and better.

Delphi
    You will keep up or face the conse-
quences.

Ludo Bagman
    The perils are plentiful, but the prizes
are palpable. Who will fight their way
through? Who will fall at the final
hurdle? What heroes do we have within
our midst? Only time will tell, ladies and
gentlemen, only time will tell.

**They move through the maze,
Scorpius and Albus being compelled**

by Delphi. As she moves ahead, the boys have a chance to talk.

Scorpius
Albus, we need to do something.

Albus
I know but what? She has snapped our wands, we're bound and she's threatening to kill you.

Scorpius
I'm ready to die if it'll stop Voldemort returning.

Albus
Are you?

Scorpius
You won't have to mourn me for long, she'll kill me and quickly kill you too.

Albus **(desperate)**
The flaw in the Time-Turner, the five-minute rule. We do all we can to run down the clock.

Scorpius
It won't work.

Act Three   Scene Twenty

As another hedge changes direction, Delphi pulls Albus and Scorpius in after her. They continue through this maze of despair.

Ludo Bagman
Now let me remind you of the current standings! Tied in first place – Mr Cedric Diggory and Mr Harry Potter. In second place – Mr Viktor Krum! And in third place – sacré bleu, Miss Fleur Delacour.

Suddenly, Albus and Scorpius emerge from behind a maze, they're running.

Albus
Where did she go?

Scorpius
Does it matter? Which way do you think?

Delphi rises up after them. She's flying, and without a broom.

Delphi
You poor creatures.

She throws the boys to the ground.

Thinking you can escape me.

Albus **(astonished)**
You're not – even on a broom.

Delphi
Brooms – such unwieldy unnecessary objects. Three minutes gone. We have two minutes left. And you will do what you're told.

Scorpius
No. We won't.

Delphi
You think you can fight me?

Scorpius
No. But we can defy you. If we lay down our lives to do so.

Delphi
The prophecy must be fulfilled. We will fulfil it.

Scorpius
Prophecies can be broken.

Act Three   Scene Twenty

Delphi
   You're mistaken child, prophecies are the future.

Scorpius
   But if the prophecy is inevitable why are we here trying to influence it? Your actions contradict your thoughts – you're dragging us through this maze because you believe this prophecy needs to be enabled – and by that logic prophecies can also be broken – prevented.

Delphi
   You talk too much, child. Crucio!

Scorpius is racked with pain.

Albus
   Scorpius!

Scorpius
   You wanted a test, Albus – this is it, and we're going to pass it.

Albus looks at Scorpius, finally aware what he has to do. He nods.

Delphi
Then you will die.

Albus **(full of strength)**
Yes. We will. And we'll do so gladly knowing it's stopped you.

Delphi rises up, full of fury.

Delphi
We don't have time for this. Cru—

Mysterious Voice
Expelliarmus!

Bang. Delphi's wand is pulled away from her. Scorpius looks on in astonishment.

Brachiabindo!

And Delphi is bound. Scorpius and Albus then turn as one and stare in astonishment at where the bolt came from: from a young, good-looking lad of seventeen or so, Cedric.

Cedric
Come no further.

Scorpius
    But you're . . .

Cedric
    Cedric Diggory. I heard screaming, I
had to come. Name yourselves, beasts, I
can fight you.

Albus wheels around, astonished.

Albus
    Cedric?

Scorpius
    You saved us.

Cedric
    Are you also a task? An obstacle?
Speak. Do I have to defeat you too?

There's a silence.

Scorpius
    No. You just have to free us. That's
the task.

**Cedric thinks, trying to work out
whether it's a trap, and then waves
his wand.**

Cedric
  Emancipare! Emancipare!

The boys are freed.

And now I can go on? Finish the maze?

The boys look at Cedric – heart-broken.

Albus
  I'm afraid you have to finish the maze.

Cedric
  Then I shall.

Cedric walks confidently away. Albus looks after him – desperate to say something, unsure what to say.

Albus
  Cedric—

Cedric turns towards him.

Your dad loves you very much.

404

Act Three Scene Twenty

Cedric
What?

Behind them, Delphi's body creeps into movement. She crawls along the ground.

Albus
Just thought you should know that.

Cedric
Okay. Um. Thank you.

Cedric looks at Albus a moment more, and then walks on. Delphi pulls out the Time-Turner from within her robes.

Scorpius
Albus.

Albus
No. Wait . . .

Scorpius
The Time Turner is spinning . . . look at what she's doing . . . she can't leave us behind.

Albus and Scorpius both scramble to grab part of the Time-Turner.

And there is a giant whoosh of light. A smash of noise.

And time stops. And then it turns over, thinks a bit, and begins spooling backwards, slow at first . . .

And then it speeds up.

Albus . . .

Albus
What have we done?

Scorpius
We had to go with the Time-Turner, we had to try to stop her.

Delphi
Stop me? How do you think you've stopped me? I am done with this. You may have destroyed my chances of using Cedric to darken the world but maybe you're right Scorpius – maybe prophecies can be prevented, maybe prophecies can be broken. What is undoubtedly true is

406

Act Three Scene Twenty

I'm done with trying to use you annoying, incompetent creatures for anything. No more wasting precious seconds on either of you. Time to try something new.

She crushes the Time-Turner. It explodes into a thousand pieces.

Delphi ascends again into the air. She laughs in delight as she sets off, hard away.

The boys try to chase her, but they've not the slightest chance. She flies, they run.

Albus
No . . . no . . . you can't . . .

Scorpius turns back and tries to pick up the Time-Turner pieces.

The Time-Turner? It's destroyed?

Scorpius
Utterly. We're stuck here. In time. Wherever in time we are. Whatever it is she's planning to do.

Albus
    Hogwarts looks the same.

Scorpius
    Yes. And we can't be seen here. Let's get out of here before we're spotted.

Albus
    We need to stop her, Scorpius.

Scorpius
    I know we do – but how?

———

Act Three

Scene Twenty-One

St Oswald's Home for Old Witches and Wizards, Delphi's Room

Harry, Hermione, Ron, Draco and Ginny look around a simple oak-panelled room.

Harry
It must have been a Confundus Charm she used on him. Used on them all. She faked being a nurse, she faked being his niece.

Hermione
I've just checked in with the Ministry – but there's no record of her. She's a shadow.

Draco
Specialis Revelio!

Everyone turns to look at Draco.

Well, it was worth a try, what are you waiting for? We know nothing, so we just have to hope this room reveals something.

Ginny
Where can she have hidden anything? It's quite a spartan room.

Ron
These panels, these panels must conceal something.

Draco
Or the bed.

Draco starts examining the bed, Ginny a lamp, as the rest start examining the panels.

Ron **(shouting as he hammers on the walls)**
What you hiding? What you got?

Act Three Scene Twenty-One

Hermione
    Maybe we should all stop for a moment and have a think about what—

Ginny unscrews a lamp chimney from an oil lamp. There's a breathing-out noise. And then hissing words. They all turn towards it.

    What was that?

Harry
    That's – I'm not supposed to be understanding – that's Parseltongue.

Hermione
    And what does it say?

Harry
    How do I . . . ? I haven't been able to understand Parseltongue since Voldemort died.

Hermione
    And nor has your scar hurt.

Harry looks at Hermione.

Part Two

Harry
It says 'welcome Augurey'. I think I need to tell it to open . . .

Draco
Then do it.

Harry shuts his eyes. He speaks in Parseltongue.

The room transforms around them, becoming darker, and more desperate. A writhing mass of painted snakes emerges on all the walls.

And on them, written in fluorescent paint, a prophecy.

What is this?

Ron
'When spares are spared, when time is turned, when unseen children murder their fathers: then will the Dark Lord return.'

Act Three Scene Twenty-One

Ginny
A prophecy. A new prophecy.

Hermione
Cedric – Cedric was called a spare.

Ron
When time is turned – she has that Time-Turner doesn't she?

Their faces sink.

Hermione
She must do.

Ron
But why does she need Scorpius or Albus?

Harry
Because I'm a parent – who hasn't seen his child. Hasn't understood his child.

Draco
Who is she? To be so obsessed with all this?

Ginny
     I think I've got the answer to that.

They all turn to her. She points up . . . their collective faces sink further and fill with fear.

Words are revealed on all the walls of the auditorium – dangerous words, horrible words.

'I will rebirth the Dark. I will bring my father back.'

Ron
     No. She can't . . .

Hermione
     How is it even – possible?

Draco
     Voldemort had a daughter?

They look up terrified. Ginny takes Harry's hand.

Act Three   Scene Twenty-One

Harry
 No, no, no. Not that. Anything but
that.

We cut to black.

———

Interval

Part Two
Act Four

Act Four
Scene One

Ministry of Magic, Grand Meeting Room

Wizards and witches from all over cram into the grand meeting room. Hermione walks on to a hastily made stage. She raises her hand for silence. Silence falls. She's surprised at the lack of effort it took. She looks around herself.

Hermione
    Thank you. I'm so pleased so many of you were able to make my – second – Extraordinary General Meeting. I've got some things to say – I ask that we deal with questions – and there will be a lot of questions – after I speak.

As many of you know, a body has been found at Hogwarts. His name was Craig Bowker. He was a good boy. We have no firm information who was responsible for the act but yesterday we searched St Oswald's. A room there revealed two things: one, a prophecy that promised . . . the return of darkness – two, written on the ceiling, a proclamation – that the Dark Lord had a – that Voldemort had a child.

The news reverberates around the room.

We don't know the full details. We're only just investigating – questioning those with a Death Eater connection . . . and as yet no record has been found either of the child or of the prophecy, but, it does look like there's some truth to it. This child was kept hidden from the wizarding world, and now she's – well now she's—

Professor McGonagall
She? A daughter? He had a daughter?

Act Four   Scene One

Hermione
    Yes. A daughter.

Professor McGonagall
    And is she now in custody?

Harry
    Professor, she did ask for no questions.

Hermione
    It's fine, Harry. No, Professor, that's where this gets worse. I'm afraid we've no means of taking her into custody. Or indeed, stopping her doing anything.
    She's out of our reach.

Professor McGonagall
    We can't – look for her?

Hermione
    We have good reason to believe she's hidden herself – in time.

Professor McGonagall
    Of all the reckless stupid things, you've kept the Time-Turner even now?

Hermione
    Professor, I assure you—

Professor McGonagall
    Shame on you, Hermione Granger!

Hermione flinches in the face of the anger.

Harry
    No, she doesn't deserve that. You have a right to be angry. You all do. But this is not all Hermione's fault. We don't know how the witch got hold of the Time-Turner. Whether my son gave it to her.

Ginny
    Whether our son gave it her. Or whether it was stolen from him.

Ginny joins Harry on the stage.

Professor McGonagall
    Your solidarity is admirable, but it doesn't make your negligence negligible.

Draco
    Then it's a negligence I too should face.

Act Four   Scene One

Draco walks up to the stage and stands beside Ginny. This is almost a Spartacus moment. There are gasps.

Hermione and Harry have done nothing wrong but try and protect us all. If they're guilty, then I am too.

Hermione looks across at her cohort – moved. Ron joins them on the stage.

Ron
   Just to say – I didn't know about much of it so can't take responsibility – and I'm pretty sure my kids had nothing to do with it – but if this lot are standing up here, then so am I.

Ginny
   No one can know where they are – whether they're together or apart. I trust that our sons will be doing all they can to stop her but . . .

Hermione
   We haven't given up. We've gone to the giants. The trolls. Everyone we can find. The Aurors are out flying, searching,

talking to those who know secrets,
following those who won't reveal secrets.

Harry
    But there is one truth we can't
escape: that somewhere in our past a
witch is trying to rewrite everything we
ever knew – and all we can do is wait –
wait for the moment she either succeeds
or fails.

Professor McGonagall
    And if she succeeds?

Harry
    Then – just like that – most of the
people in this room will be gone, we'll
no longer exist and Voldemort will rule
again.

———

Act Four
Scene Two

Scottish Highlands, Aviemore Train Station, 1981

Albus and Scorpius are looking at a Station Master, apprehensively.

Albus
   One of us should talk to him, don't you think?

Scorpius
   Hello, Mr Station Master. Mr Muggle. Question: did you see a flying witch passing here? And by the way, what year is it? We just ran away from Hogwarts because we were frightened of upsetting things, but this is okay?

Albus

    You know what annoys me most of all? Dad will think we did it deliberately.

Scorpius

    Albus. Really? I mean, really really? We're – trapped – lost – in time – probably permanently – and you're worrying what your dad might think about it? I will never understand the two of you.

Albus

    There's a lot to understand. Dad's pretty complicated.

Scorpius

    And you're not? Not to question your taste in women but you fancied . . . well . . .

They both know who he's talking about.

Albus

    I did, didn't I? I mean what she did to Craig . . .

Scorpius

Let's not think about that. Let's focus on the fact that we have no wands, no brooms, no means of returning to our time, all we have is our wits and – no, that's all, our wits – and we have to stop her.

Station Master (in very strong Scots)

Ye ken th' Auld Reekie train is running late, boys?

Scorpius

Sorry?

Station Master

If you're waiting oan th' Auld Reekie train, you'll need tae ken it's running late. Train wirks oan th' line. It's a' oan th' amended time buird.

He looks at them, they look back bewildered. He frowns and hands them an amended timetable. He points to the right bit of it.

Late.

**Albus takes it and examines it.
His face changes as he takes in
enormous information. Scorpius just
stares at the Station Master.**

Albus
I know where she is.

Scorpius
You understood that?

Albus
Look at the date. On the timetable.

Scorpius leans in and reads.

Scorpius
The thirtieth of October 1981. Day
before Hallows' Eve, thirty-nine years
ago. But – why is she? Oh.

**Scorpius's face falls as he
realises.**

Albus
The death of my grandparents. The
attack on my dad as a baby . . . the
moment when Voldemort's curse
rebounded on himself. She's not trying

428

to bring about her prophecy – she's trying to prevent the big one.

Scorpius
  The big one?

Albus
  'The one with the power to vanquish the Dark Lord approaches . . .

Scorpius joins in.

Scorpius **and** Albus
  '. . . born to those who have thrice defied him, born as the seventh month dies . . .'

Scorpius's face falls with every word.

Scorpius
  It's my fault. I told her that prophecies can be broken – I told her the whole logic of prophecies is questionable—

Albus
  In twenty-four hours' time Voldemort curses himself trying to kill the baby

Harry Potter. Delphi is trying to prevent that curse. She's going to kill Harry herself. We need to get to Godric's Hollow. Now.

Act Four
Scene Three

Godric's Hollow, 1981

**Albus and Scorpius walk through
the centre of Godric's Hollow and
it's a bustling, beautiful little village.**

Scorpius
    Well, there's no visible signs of attack
that I can see . . .

Albus
    This is Godric's Hollow?

Scorpius
    Your dad's never taken you?

Albus
    No, he tried to a few times but I
refused.

Scorpius
    Well there's no time for a tour – we have a murderous witch to save the world from – but regard . . . the church, St Jerome's . . .

As he indicates a church becomes visible.

Albus
    It's magnificent.

Scorpius
    And St Jerome's graveyard is supposedly magnificently haunted **(he points in another direction)**, and that's where the statue of Harry and his parents will be—

Albus
    My dad has a statue?

Scorpius
    Oh. Not yet. But he will. Hopefully. And this – this house is where Bathilda Bagshot lived, lives . . .

Albus
    The Bathilda Bagshot? **A History of Magic** Bathilda Bagshot?

Act Four Scene Three

Scorpius
  The very same. Oh my, that's her. Wow. Squeak. My geekness is a-quivering.

Albus
  Scorpius!

Scorpius
  And here it is—

Albus
  The home of James, Lily and Harry Potter . . .

A young, attractive couple leave a house with a baby in a pushchair. Albus moves towards them, Scorpius pulls him back.

Scorpius
  They can't see you, Albus, it might damage time, and we're not doing that – not this time.

Albus
  But this means, she hasn't . . . we've made it . . . she hasn't . . .

Scorpius
    So what do we do now? Get ready to fight her? Because she's pretty . . . fierce.

Albus
    Yes. We haven't really thought this one through have we? What do we do now? How do we protect my dad?

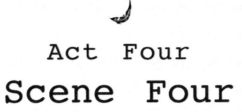

Act Four
Scene Four

Ministry of Magic, Harry's Office

Harry is hurriedly going through paperwork.

Dumbledore
Good evening, Harry.

Beat. Harry looks up at the portrait of Dumbledore, his face passive.

Harry
Professor Dumbledore. In my office, I'm honoured. I must be where the action is, tonight?

Dumbledore
What are you doing?

Harry

Going through papers, seeing if I've missed anything I shouldn't have. Marshalling forces to fight in the limited way we can fight. Knowing that the battle is being raged far away from us. What else can I do?

Pause. Dumbledore says nothing.

Where have you been, Dumbledore?

Dumbledore

I'm here now.

Harry

Here just as the battle is lost. Or are you denying that Voldemort is going to return?

Dumbledore

It is – possible.

Harry

Go. Leave. I don't want you here, I don't need you. You were absent every time it really counted. I fought him three times without you. I'll face him again, if needs be – alone.

Act Four Scene Four

Dumbledore

Harry, don't you think I wanted to fight him on your behalf? I would have spared you if I could—

Harry

Love blinds us? Do you even know what that means? Do you even know how bad that advice was? My son is – my son is fighting battles for us just as I had to for you. And I have proved as bad a father to him as you were to me. Leaving him in places he felt unloved – growing in him resentments he'll take years to understand—

Dumbledore

If you're referring to Privet Drive then—

Harry

Years – years I spent there alone, without knowing what I was, or why I was there, without knowing that anybody cared!

Dumbledore

I – did not wish to become attached to you—

Part Two

Harry
    Protecting yourself, even then!

Dumbledore
    No. I was protecting you. I did not
want to hurt you . . .

**Dumbledore attempts to reach
out of the portrait, but he can't.
He begins to cry but tries to hide it.**

    But I had to meet you in the
end . . . eleven years old, and you were
so brave. So good. You walked uncom-
plainingly along the path that had been
laid at your feet. Of course I loved
you . . . and I knew that it would
happen all over again . . . that where I
loved, I would cause irreparable
damage . . . I am no fit person to
love . . . I have never loved without
causing harm . . .

    Beat.

Harry
    You would have hurt me less if you
had told me this, then.

Act Four Scene Four

Dumbledore (openly weeping now)
I was blind. That is what love does. I couldn't see that you needed to hear that this closed-up, tricky, dangerous old man . . . loved you . . .

A pause. The two men are overcome with emotion.

Harry
It isn't true that I never complained.

Dumbledore
Harry, there is never a perfect answer in this messy, emotional world. Perfection is beyond the reach of humankind, beyond the reach of magic. In every shining moment of happiness is that drop of poison: the knowledge that pain will come again. Be honest to those you love, show your pain. To suffer is as human as to breathe.

Harry
You said that to me once before.

Dumbledore
It is all I have to offer you tonight.

439

He begins to walk away.

Harry
    Don't go!

Dumbledore
    Those that we love never truly leave us, Harry. There are things that death cannot touch. Paint . . . and memory . . . and love.

Harry
    I loved you too, Dumbledore.

Dumbledore
    I know.

He is gone. And Harry is alone. Draco enters.

Draco
    Did you know that in this other reality – the reality Scorpius saw into – I was Head of Magical Law Enforcement? Maybe this room will be mine soon enough. Are you okay?

Harry is consumed in his grief.

Act Four Scene Four

Harry
Come in – I'll give you the tour.

**Draco walks hesitantly inside the
room. He looks around distastefully.**

Draco
The thing is though – never really
fancied being a Ministry man. Even as a
child. My dad – it's all he ever wanted –
me, no.

Harry
What did you want to do?

Draco
Quidditch. But I wasn't good enough.
Mainly I wanted to be happy.

**Harry nods. Draco looks at him a
second more.**

Sorry, I'm not very good at small
talk, do you mind if we skip on to the
serious business?

Harry
Of course. What – serious –
business?

Beat.

Draco
　　Do you think Theodore Nott had the only Time-Turner?

Harry
　　What?

Draco
　　The Time-Turner the Ministry seized was a prototype. Made of inexpensive metal. It does the job, sure. But only being able to go back in time for five minutes – that's a serious flaw – it isn't something you'd sell to true collectors of Dark Magic.

Harry realises what Draco is saying.

Harry
　　He was working for you?

Draco
　　No. My father. He liked owning things that no one else had. The Ministry's Time-Turners – thanks to Croaker – were always a little vanilla for him. He wanted

the ability to go back further than an hour, he wanted the ability to travel back years. He'd never have used it, secretly I think he preferred a world without Voldemort. But yes, the Time-Turner was built for him.

Harry
    And did you keep it?

Draco reveals the Time-Turner.

Draco
    No five-minute problem, and it gleams like gold, just the way the Malfoys like it. You're smiling.

Harry
    Hermione Granger. It was the reason she kept the first, the fear that there might be a second. Hanging on to this, you could have been sent to Azkaban.

Draco
    Consider the alternative – consider if people had known that I had the ability to travel in time. Consider the rumour that would have been given increased – credence.

443

**Harry looks at Draco, under-
standing him perfectly.**

Harry
   Scorpius.

Draco
   We were capable of having children,
but Astoria was frail. A blood maledic-
tion, a serious one. An ancestor was
cursed . . . it showed up in her. You
know how these things can resurface
after generations . . .

Harry
   I'm sorry, Draco.

Draco
   I didn't want to risk her health, I
said it didn't matter whether the Malfoy
line died with me – whatever my father
said. But Astoria – she didn't want a
baby for the Malfoy name, for pure
blood or glory, but for us. Our child,
Scorpius was born . . . it was the best
day of both our lives, although it weak-
ened Astoria considerably. We hid
ourselves away, the three of us. I

444

Act Four Scene Four

wanted to conserve her strength . . .
and so the rumours started.

Harry
 I can't imagine what that was like.

Draco
 Astoria always knew that she was not
destined for old age. She wanted me to
have somebody when she left,
because . . . it is exceptionally lonely,
being Draco Malfoy. I will always be
suspected. There is no escaping the
past. I never realised, though, that by
hiding him away from this gossiping,
judgemental world, I ensured that my
son would emerge shrouded in worse
suspicion than I ever endured.

Harry
 Love blinds. We have both tried to
give our sons not what they needed, but
what we needed. We've been so busy
trying to rewrite our own pasts, we've
blighted their present.

Draco
 Which is why you need this. I have
been holding on to it, barely resisting

445

using it, even though I would sell my soul for another minute with Astoria . . .

Harry
    Oh, Draco . . . we can't. We can't use it.

Draco looks up at Harry, and for the first time – at the bottom of this dreadful pit – they look at each other as friends.

Draco
    We have to find them – if it takes centuries, we must find our sons . . .

Harry
    We have no idea where they are or when they are. Searching in time when you've no idea where in time to search, that's a fool's errand. No, love won't do it and nor will a Time-Turner, I'm afraid. It's up to our sons now – they're the only ones who can save us.

Act Four
Scene Five

Godric's Hollow, Outside James and Lily Potter's House, 1981

Albus
We tell my granddad and grandma?

Scorpius
That they'll never get to see their son grow up?

Albus
She's strong enough – I know she is – you saw her.

Scorpius
She looked wonderful, Albus. And if I were you I'd be desperate to talk to her. But she needs to be able to beg

Voldemort for Harry's life, she needs to think he might die, and you're the worst spoiler in the world that didn't turn out to be true . . .

Albus
    Dumbledore. Dumbledore's alive. We get Dumbledore involved. We do what you did with Snape—

Scorpius
    Can we risk him knowing your dad survives? That he has kids?

Albus
    He's Dumbledore! He can cope with anything!

Scorpius
    Albus, there have been about a hundred books written on what Dumbledore knew, how he knew it or why he did what he did. But what's undoubtedly true – what he did – he needs to do – and I'm not going to risk messing with it. I was able to ask for help because I was in an alternate reality. We aren't. We're in the past. We can't fix time only to create more

problems – if our adventures have taught us anything, they've taught us that. The dangers of talking to anyone – infecting time – are too great.

Albus

So we need to – talk to the future. We need to send Dad a message.

Scorpius

But we don't have an owl that can fly through time. And he doesn't have a Time-Turner.

Albus

We get a message to Dad. He'll find a way to get back here. Even if he has to build a Time-Turner himself.

Scorpius

We send a memory – like a Pensieve – stand over him and send a message, hope he reaches for the memory at exactly the right moment. I mean, it's unlikely, but . . . stand over the baby – and just repeatedly shout help. Help. Help. I mean, it might traumatise the baby slightly.

Albus
  Only slightly.

Scorpius
  A bit of trauma now is nothing compared to what's happening . . . and maybe when he then thinks – later – he might remember the faces of us as we – shouted—

Albus
  Help.

Scorpius looks at Albus.

Scorpius
  You're right. It's a terrible idea.

Albus
  It's one of your worst ideas ever.

Scorpius
  Got it! We deliver it ourselves – we wait forty years – we deliver it—

Albus
  Not a chance – once Delphi has set time the way she wants she'll send armies to try and find us – kill us—

Act Four   Scene Five

Scorpius
So we hide in a hole?

Albus
As pleasurable as it will be to hide in a hole with you for the next forty years . . . they'll find us. And we'll die and time will be stuck in the wrong position. No. We need something we can control, something we know he'll get at exactly the right time. We need a . . .

Scorpius
There's nothing. Still, if I had to choose a companion to be at the return of eternal darkness with, I'd choose you.

Albus
No offence, but I'd choose someone massive and really good at magic.

Lily exits the house with Baby Harry in a pram, she carefully puts a blanket on him.

His blanket. She's wrapping him in his blanket.

Scorpius
    Well, it is a moderately cold day.

Albus
    He always said – it's the only thing he had from her. Look at the love with which she's put it on him – I think he'd like to know about that – I wish I could tell him.

Scorpius
    And I wish I could tell my dad – well, I'm not sure what. I think I'd like to tell him that I'm occasionally capable of more bravery than he might think I am.

Albus has a thought.

Albus
    Scorpius – my dad still has that blanket.

Scorpius
    That won't work. If we write a message on it now, even really small, he'll read it too soon. Time will be spoilt.

Act Four   Scene Five

Albus

What do you know about love potions? What's the ingredient they all contain?

Scorpius

Amongst other things, Pearl Dust.

Albus

Pearl Dust is a relatively rare ingredient isn't it?

Scorpius

Mainly because it's pretty expensive. What's this about, Albus?

Albus

Dad and I had a fight on the day before I went to school.

Scorpius

This I am aware of. I believe it kind of got us into this mess.

Albus

I threw the blanket across the room. It collided with the love potion that Uncle Ron gave me as a joke.

Scorpius

He's a funny guy.

Albus

The potion spilt and the blanket was covered in it and I happen to know for a fact Mum hasn't let Dad touch that room since I left it.

Scorpius

So?

Albus

So it's coming up to Hallows' Eve in their time as well as ours – and he told me he always finds that blanket, he needs to be with it on Hallows' Eve – it was the last thing his mum gave him – so he will look for it and when he finds it . . .

Scorpius

No. Still not getting you.

Albus

What reacts with Pearl Dust?

Scorpius

Well, it is said that if Tincture of

Act Four   Scene Five

Demiguise and Pearl Dust meet . . .
they burn.

Albus
　　And is Tincture of **(he's unsure how
to say the word)** Demiguise visible to
the naked eye?

Scorpius
　　No.

Albus
　　So if we were to get that blanket and
write on it in Tincture of Demiguise
then . . .

Scorpius **(eureka)**
　　Nothing would react to it until it
came into contact with the love potion.
In your room. In the present. By
Dumbledore, I love it.

Albus
　　We just need to work out where to
find some . . . Demiguises.

Scorpius
　　You know, rumour has it Bathilda

Part Two

Bagshot never saw the point in witches and wizards locking their doors.

The door swings open.

Rumour was right. Time to steal some wands and get potioning.

———

Act Four
Scene Six

Harry and Ginny Potter's House, Albus's Room

Harry is sitting on Albus's bed. Ginny enters, she looks at him.

Ginny
Surprised to find you here.

Harry
Don't worry, I haven't touched anything. Your shrine is preserved. **(He winces.)** Sorry. Bad choice of words.

Ginny says nothing. Harry looks up at her.

You know I've had some pretty
terrible Hallows' Eves – but this is
undoubtedly at least the – second worst.

Ginny
    I was wrong – to blame you – I
always accuse you of jumping to things
and it was me who – Albus went
missing and I assumed it was your fault.
I'm sorry I did that.

Harry
    You don't think this is my fault?

Ginny
    Harry, he was kidnapped by a
powerful Dark witch, how can that be
your fault?

Harry
    I chased him away. I chased him to
her.

Ginny
    Can we not treat this as if the battle
is already lost?

Ginny nods. Harry starts to cry.

Act Four   Scene Six

Harry
    I'm sorry Gin—

Ginny
    Are you not listening to me? I'm
sorry too.

Harry
    I shouldn't have survived – it was my
destiny to die – even Dumbledore
thought so – and yet I lived. I beat
Voldemort. All these people – all these
people – my parents, Fred, the Fallen
Fifty – and it's me that gets to live?
How is that? All this damage – and it's
my fault.

Ginny
    They were killed by Voldemort.

Harry
    But if I'd stopped him sooner? All
that blood on my hands. And now our
son has been taken too—

Ginny
    He's not dead. Do you hear me
Harry? He's not dead.

Part Two

She takes Harry in her arms. There is a big pause filled with pure unhappiness.

Harry
The Boy Who Lived. How many people have to die for the Boy Who Lived?

Harry sways a moment, unsure. Then he notices the blanket. He walks towards it.

This blanket is all I have you know . . . of that Hallows' Eve. This is all I have to remember them. And whilst—

He picks up the blanket. He discovers it has holes in it. He looks at it, dismayed.

This has got holes in it. Ron's idiotic love potion has burnt through it, right through it. Look at this. It's ruined. Ruined.

He opens up the blanket. He sees writing burnt through it. He's surprised.

Act Four   Scene Six

What?

Ginny
   Harry, it has – something –
written—

**On another part of the stage
Albus and Scorpius appear.**

Albus
   'Dad . . .'

Scorpius
   We're starting with 'Dad'?

Albus
   So he'll know it's from me.

Scorpius
   Harry is his name. We should start
with 'Harry'.

Albus **(firm)**
   We're starting with 'Dad'.

Harry
   'Dad', does it say 'Dad'? It's not that
distinct . . .

Scorpius
 'Dad, help.'

Ginny
 'Hello'? Does that say 'Hello'? And
then . . . 'Good' . . .

Harry
 'Dad Hello Good Hello'? No. This
is . . . a strange joke.

Albus
 'Dad. Help. Godric's Hollow.'

Ginny
 Give me that. My eyesight is better
than yours. Yes. 'Dad Hello Good' –
that's not 'Hello' again – that's 'Hallow'
or 'Hollow'? And then some numbers –
these are clearer – '3 . . . 1 . . . 1 . . .
0 . . . 8 . . . 1'. Is this one of those
Muggle telephone numbers? Or a grid
reference or a . . .

**Harry looks up, several
thoughts smashing through his brain
at once.**

Harry
No. It's a date. 31 October 1981. The date my parents were killed.

Ginny looks at Harry, and then back at the blanket.

Ginny
That doesn't say 'Hello'. It says 'Help'.

Harry
'Dad. Help. Godric's Hollow. 31/10/81.' It's a message. Clever boy left me a message.

Harry kisses Ginny hard.

Ginny
Albus wrote this?

Harry
And he's told me where they are and when they are, and now we know where she is, we know where we can fight her.

He kisses her hard again.

Ginny
We haven't got them back again yet.

Part Two

Harry
   I'll send an owl to Hermione. You send one to Draco. Tell them to meet us at Godric's Hollow with the Time-Turner.

Ginny
   And it is 'us', okay? Don't even think about going back without me, Harry.

Harry
   Of course you're coming. We have a chance Ginny, and by Dumbledore – that's all that we need – a chance.

Act Four
Scene Seven

Godric's Hollow

Ron, Hermione, Draco, Harry and Ginny walk through a present-day Godric's Hollow. A busy market town (it's expanded over the years).

Hermione
Godric's Hollow. It must be twenty years . . .

Ginny
Is it just me or are there more Muggles about?

Hermione
It's become quite popular as a weekend break.

465

Draco
I can see why – look at the thatched roofs. And is that a farmers' market?

Hermione approaches Harry – who is looking around himself, overwhelmed by all he is seeing.

Hermione
You remember when we were last here? This feels just like old times.

Ron
Old times with a few unwelcome ponytails added to the mix.

Draco knows a barb when he hears one.

Draco
Can I just say . . .

Ron
Malfoy, you may be all chummy chummy with Harry, and you may have produced a relatively nice child, but you've said some very unfair things to and about my wife . . .

Act Four Scene Seven

Hermione

And your wife doesn't need you fighting her battles for her.

Hermione looks witheringly at Ron. Ron takes the hit.

Ron

Fine. But if you say one thing about her or me . . .

Draco

You'll do what, Weasley?

Hermione

He'll hug you. Because we're all on the same team, aren't we Ron?

Ron (hesitating in the face of her unwavering gaze)

Fine. I, um, I think you've got really nice hair. Draco.

Hermione

Thank you, husband. Now this seems a good spot. Let's do this . . .

**Draco takes out the Time-Turner –
it begins spinning wildly as the others
take their places around it.**

**And there is a giant whoosh of
light. A smash of noise.**

**And time stops. And then it turns
over, thinks a bit, and begins spooling
backwards, slow at first . . .**

And then it speeds up.

They look around themselves.

Ron
    So? Has it worked?

Act Four
SCENE EIGHT

Godric's Hollow, A Shed, 1981

Albus looks up amazed to see Ginny and then Harry, and then he takes in the rest of the happy band (Ron, Draco and Hermione).

Albus
  Mum?

Harry
  Albus Severus Potter. Are we pleased to see you.

Albus runs and throws himself into Ginny's arms. Ginny receives him, delighted.

Part Two

Albus
    You got our note . . . ?

Ginny
    We got your note.

Scorpius trots up to his dad.

Draco
    We can hug too if you like . . .

**Scorpius looks at his dad, unsure
for a moment. And then they sort of
half-hug in a very awkward way.
Draco smiles.**

Ron
    Now, where's this Delphi?

Scorpius
    You know about Delphi?

Albus
    She's here – she's trying to kill you
we think. Before Voldemort curses
himself. She's going to kill you and so
break the prophecy and . . .

Hermione
Yes, we thought that might be it too.
Do you know where specifically she is
now?

Scorpius
She's disappeared. How did you –
how did you without the
Time-Turner . . .

Harry **(interrupting)**
That's a long and complicated
story, Scorpius. And we don't have time
for it.

Draco smiles at Harry gratefully.

Hermione
Harry's right. Time is of the essence.
We need to get people into position.
Now, Godric's Hollow is not a large
place, but she could be coming from any
direction. So we need somewhere that
gives us good views of the town – that
allows for multiple and clear observation
points – and that will, most importantly,
keep us hidden because we cannot risk
being seen.

Part Two

They all frown, thinking.

I'd say St Jerome's Church ticks all those boxes wouldn't you?

———

Act Four
Scene Nine

Godric's Hollow, Church, Sanctuary, 1981

Albus is sleeping in a pew. Ginny watches him carefully. Harry is looking out the opposite window.

Harry
    No. Nothing. Why isn't she here?

Ginny
    We're together, your mum and dad are alive, we can turn time Harry, we can't speed it up. She'll come when she's ready and we'll be ready for her.

She looks at Albus's sleeping form.

Or some of us will be.

473

Harry
Poor kid thought he had to save the
world.

Ginny
Poor kid has saved the world. That
blanket was masterful. I mean, he also
almost destroyed the world, but probably
best not to focus on that bit.

Harry
You think he's okay?

Ginny
He's getting there, it just might take
him a bit of time – and you a bit of
time too.

**Harry smiles. She looks back at
Albus. He does too.**

You know, after I'd opened the
Chamber of Secrets – after Voldemort
had bewitched me with that terrible
diary and I'd almost destroyed
everything—

Harry
I remember.

Act Four   Scene Nine

Ginny

After I came out of hospital –
everyone ignored me, shut me out –
other than, that is, the boy who had
everything – who came across the
Gryffindor common room and challenged
me to a game of Exploding Snap. People
think they know all there is to know
about you, but the best bits of you are
– have always been – heroic in really
quiet ways. My point is – after this is
over, just remember if you could – that
sometimes people – but particularly children – just want someone to play
Exploding Snap with.

Harry

You think that's what we're missing –
Exploding Snap?

Ginny

No. But the love I felt from you that
day – I'm not sure Albus feels that.

Harry

I'd do anything for him.

Ginny

Harry, you'd do anything for anybody.

You were pretty happy to sacrifice yourself for the world. He needs to feel
specific love. It'll make him stronger,
and you stronger too.

Harry
    You know, it wasn't until we thought
Albus had gone that I truly understood
what my mother was able to do for me.
A counter-charm so powerful that it was
able to repel the spell of death.

Ginny
    And the only spell Voldemort couldn't
understand – love.

Harry
    I do love him specifically, Ginny.

Ginny
    I know, but he needs to feel it.

Harry
    I'm lucky to have you aren't I?

Ginny
    Extremely. And I'd be delighted to
discuss just how lucky at another time. But
for now – let's focus on stopping Delphi.

Harry
    We are running out of time.

A thought occurs to Ginny.

Ginny
    Unless – Harry, has anyone thought – why has she picked now? Today?

Harry
    Because this is the day that everything changed . . .

Ginny
    Right now you're over a year old, am I right?

Harry
    A year and three months.

Ginny
    That's a year and three months she could have killed you in. Even now, she's been in Godric's Hollow for twenty-four hours. What's she waiting for?

Harry
    I'm still not entirely following—

Ginny
What if she's not waiting for you –
she's waiting for him . . . to stop him?

Harry
What?

Ginny
Delphi's picked tonight because he's
here – because her father is coming.
She wants to meet him. Be with him,
the father she loves. Voldemort's problems started when he attacked you. If
he hadn't done that . . .

Harry
He'd have only got more powerful –
the darkness would only have got
darker.

Ginny
The best way to break the prophecy
is not to kill Harry Potter, it's to stop
Voldemort doing anything at all.

———

Act Four
Scene Ten

Godric's Hollow, Church, 1981

**The group are gathered
and full of confusion.**

Ron
    So let me get this right – we're
fighting to protect Voldemort?

Albus
    Voldemort killing my grandparents.
Voldemort trying to kill my dad?

Hermione
    Of course, Ginny. Delphi's not trying
to kill Harry – she's stopping Voldemort
trying to kill Harry. Brilliant.

Draco
So – we just wait? Until Voldemort turns up?

Albus
Does she know when he does turn up? Hasn't she come here twenty-four hours early because she isn't sure when he'll arrive and in what direction? The history books – correct me if I'm wrong, Scorpius – show nothing about when and how he arrived in Godric's Hollow?

Scorpius and Hermione
You're not wrong.

Ron
Blimey! There are two of them!

Draco
So how can we use this to our advantage?

Albus
Do you know what I'm really good at?

Harry
There's plenty you're good at, Albus.

Act Four   Scene Ten

Albus

Polyjuicing. And I think Bathilda Bagshot may have all the ingredients for Polyjuice in her basement. We can Polyjuice into Voldemort and bring her to us.

Ron

To use Polyjuice you need a bit of someone. We don't have a bit of Voldemort.

Hermione

But I like the concept, a pretend mouse for her cat.

Harry

How close can we get through transfiguration?

Hermione

We know what he looks like. We've got some excellent wizards and witches here.

Ginny

You want to transfigure into Voldemort?

Albus
It's the only way.

Hermione
It is, isn't it?

Ron steps forward bravely.

Ron
Then I would like to – I think I should be him. I mean, it won't be – exactly nice being Voldemort – but without wishing to blow my own trumpet – I am probably the most chilled out of all of us and . . . so maybe transfiguring into him – into the Dark Lord will do less damage to me than – any of you more – intense – people.

Harry steps away, introspective.

Hermione
Who are you calling intense?

Draco
I'd also like to volunteer. I think being Voldemort requires precision . . . no offence, Ron . . . and a knowledge of Dark Magic, and—

Act Four Scene Ten

Hermione
And I'd like to volunteer, too. As Minister for Magic I think it's my responsibility and right.

Scorpius
Maybe we should draw lots—

Draco
You're not volunteering, Scorpius.

Albus
Actually—

Ginny
No, no way. I think you're all mad. I know what that voice is like inside your head. I won't have it in mine again—

Harry
And anyway – it has to be me.

Everyone turns to Harry.

Draco
What?

Harry
For this plan to work she has to

believe it's him, without hesitation. She'll use Parseltongue – and I **knew** there was a reason why I still have that ability. But more than that, I – know what it is to feel – like him. I know what it is to **be** him. It has to be me.

Ron
　　Rubbish. Beautifully put, but beautiful rubbish. No way are you going to—

Hermione
　　I'm afraid you're right, my old friend.

Ron
　　Hermione, you're wrong, Voldemort is not something to be – Harry should not—

Ginny
　　And I hate to agree with my brother, but . . .

Ron
　　He could get stuck – as Voldemort – forever.

Hermione
　　So could any of us. Your concerns are valid but . . .

Act Four Scene Ten

Harry
Hang on, Hermione. Gin.

Ginny and Harry make eye contact.

I won't do it if you don't want me to. But it feels like the only way to me. Am I wrong?

Ginny thinks a moment and then softly nods. Harry's face hardens.

Ginny
You're right.

Harry
Then let's do this.

Draco
Don't we need to discuss the route you're taking – the—

Harry
She's watching for him. She'll come to me.

Draco
And then what? When she's with

you? May I remind you this is a very
powerful witch.

Ron
Easy. He gets her in here. We zap
her together.

Draco
'Zap her'?

Hermione looks around the room.

Hermione
We'll hide behind these doors. If you
can get her to this point Harry **(she
indicates the point where the light
from the church's Rose Window hits
the floor),** then we come out and make
sure she has no chance to escape.

Ron **(with a look to Draco)**
And then we'll **zap** her.

Hermione
Harry, last chance, are you sure you
can do this?

Harry
Yes, I can do this.

Act Four   Scene Ten

Draco
    No, there's too many what ifs – too
many things that can go wrong – the
transfiguration could not hold, she could
see through it – if she escapes us now
there's no telling the damage she can do
– we need time to properly plan to—

Albus
    Draco, trust my dad. He won't let us
down.

Harry looks at Albus – moved.

Hermione
    Wands.

**Everyone withdraws their wands.
Harry clasps his.**

**There's a light that builds – that
overwhelms.**

**The transfiguration is slow and
monstrous.**

**And the form of Voldemort
emerges from Harry. And it's
horrendous. He turns. He looks**

around his friends and family. They look back – aghast.

Ron
    Bloody hell.

Harry/Voldemort
    It worked, then?

Ginny **(gravely)**
    Yes. It worked.

———

Act Four
Scene Eleven

Godric's Hollow, Church, 1981

Ron, Hermione, Draco, Scorpius and Albus stand at the window, looking out. Ginny can't look. She sits further back.

Albus notices his mum sitting apart. He walks over to her.

Albus
It's going to be okay, you know that, Mum?

Ginny
I know it is. Or I hope I do. I just – don't want to see him like that. The man I love shrouded in the man I hate.

Part Two

Albus sits beside his mum.

Albus

I liked her, Mum. You know that? I really liked her. Delphi. And she was – Voldemort's daughter?

Ginny

That's what they're good at Albus – catching innocents in their web.

Albus

This is all my fault.

Ginny takes Albus in her arms.

Ginny

How funny. Your dad seems to think it's all his. Strange pair, you are.

Scorpius

That's her. That's her. She's seen him.

Hermione

Positions. Everybody. And remember, don't come out until he's got her in the light. We've one shot at this, we don't want to mess it up.

Act Four   Scene Eleven

They all move fast.

Draco
Hermione Granger, I'm being bossed around by Hermione Granger. **(She turns towards him, he smiles.)** And I'm mildly enjoying it.

Scorpius
Dad . . .

They scatter. They hide behind two major doors.

Harry/Voldemort re-enters the church. He walks a few paces and then he turns.

Harry/Voldemort
Whichever witch or wizard is following me, I assure you, you will regret it.

Delphi emerges behind him. She is compelled to him. This is her father and this is the moment she's waited for her entire life.

Delphi
Lord Voldemort. It is me. I am following you.

Harry/Voldemort
I do not know you. Leave me.

She breathes deeply.

Delphi
I am your daughter.

Harry/Voldemort
If you were my daughter, I'd know of you.

Delphi looks at him imploringly.

Delphi
I am from the future. The child of Bellatrix Lestrange and you. I was born in Malfoy Manor before the Battle of Hogwarts. A battle you are going to lose. I have come to save you.

Harry/Voldemort turns. She meets his eyes.

It was Rodolphus Lestrange, Bellatrix's

loyal husband, who on return from Azkaban told me who I was and revealed the prophecy he thought I was destined to fulfil. I am your daughter, sir.

Harry/Voldemort
I am familiar with Bellatrix and there are certain similarities in your face – though you haven't inherited the best of her. But without proof . . .

Delphi speaks intently in Parseltongue.

Harry/Voldemort laughs viciously.

That's your proof?

Delphi effortlessly rises into the air. Harry/Voldemort steps back – amazed.

Delphi
I am the Augurey to your Dark Lord, and I am ready to give all that I have to serve you.

Harry/Voldemort **(trying not to show his shock)**
  You learnt flight – from – me?

Delphi
  I have tried to follow the path you set.

Harry/Voldemort
  I have never met a witch or a wizard who's attempted to be my equal before.

Delphi
  Do not mistake me – I would not claim to be worthy of you, Lord. But I have devoted my life to being a child you could be proud of.

Harry/Voldemort **(interrupting)**
  I see what you are, and I see what you could be. Daughter.

  She looks at him, desperately moved.

Delphi
  Father?

Harry/Voldemort
  Together, the power we could wield.

494

Act Four Scene Eleven

Delphi
   Father . . .

Harry/Voldemort
   Come here, in the light, so I may examine what my blood made.

Delphi
   Your mission is a mistake. Attacking Harry Potter is a mistake. He will destroy you.

Harry/Voldemort's hand turns into Harry's hand. He looks at it astonished and dismayed, and then quickly pulls it inside his sleeve.

Harry/Voldemort
   He is a baby.

Delphi
   He has his mother's love, your spell will rebound, destroying you and making him too powerful and you too weak. You will recover, to spend the next seventeen years consumed in a battle with him – a battle you will lose.

Harry/Voldemort's hair begins to sprout, he feels it, he attempts to cover it. He pulls his hood over his head.

Harry/Voldemort
Then I won't attack him. You are right.

Delphi
Father?

Harry/Voldemort shrinks down – he is now more Harry than Voldemort. He turns his back to Delphi.

Father?

Harry **(trying desperately to still sound like** Voldemort**)**
Your plan is a good one. The fight is off. You have served me well, now come here into the light so I may examine you.

Delphi sees a door slightly sway open and then be pulled shut. She frowns at it, thinking rapidly, her suspicion growing.

496

Act Four   Scene Eleven

Delphi
    Father . . .

She tries to get a glimpse of his face again, there is almost a dance happening here.

You are not Lord Voldemort.

Delphi unleashes a bolt from her hand. Harry matches her.

Incendio!

Harry
    Incendio!

The bolts meet in a beautiful explosion in the middle of the room.

And with her other hand Delphi sends bolts to both doors as the others try to open them.

Delphi
    Potter. Colloportus!

Harry looks at the doors, dismayed.

What? Thought your friends were going to join you did you?

Hermione **(from off)**
  Harry . . . Harry . . .

Ginny **(from off)**
  She's sealed the doors from your side.

Harry
  Fine. I'll deal with you alone.

He moves to attack her again. But she is far stronger. Harry's wand ascends towards her. He is disarmed. He is helpless.

  How did you . . . ? What are you?

Delphi
  I've watched you for a long time, Harry Potter. I know you better than my father did.

Harry
  You think you've learnt my weaknesses?

Act Four   Scene Eleven

Delphi

I've studied to be worthy of him! Yes, even though he is the supreme wizard of all time, he will be proud of me. Expulso!

Harry rolls away as the floor explodes behind him. He crawls frantically under a church pew, trying to work out how he can fight her.

Are you crawling away from me? Harry Potter. Hero of the wizarding world. Crawling away like a rat. Wingardium Leviosa!

The church pew ascends into the air.

The question is whether it's worth my time to kill you, knowing that as soon as I stop my father, your destruction will be assured. How to decide? Oh, I'm bored, I'll kill you.

She sends down the pew hard down upon him. It smashes as he rolls desperately away.

Albus emerges from a grate on the floor, neither notice.

Avada—

Albus
Dad . . .

Harry
Albus! No!

Delphi
Two of you? Choices, choices. I think I'll kill the boy first. Avada Kedavra!

She fires the Killing Curse at Albus – but Harry throws him out of the way. The bolt smashes into the ground.

He fires a bolt back.

You think you're stronger than me?

Harry
No. I'm not.

They fire bolts mercilessly at each other as Albus rolls quickly away and

**slams a spell into one door and then
another.**

But we are.

**Albus opens both doors with his
wand.**

Albus
Alohomora! Alohomora!

Harry
I've never fought alone, you see. And
I never will.

**Hermione, Ron, Ginny and
Draco emerge from the doors,
and fire up their spells at Delphi,
who screams out in exasperation.
This is titanic. But she can't fight
them all.**

**There are a series of bangs – and
then, overwhelmed, Delphi tumbles
down to the floor.**

Delphi
No . . . No . . .

Hermione
Brachiabindo!

She's bound.

Harry advances towards Delphi. He doesn't take his eyes off her. All the others stay back.

Harry
Albus, are you okay?

Albus
Yes, Dad, I'm okay.

Harry still doesn't take his eyes off Delphi. He's still scared of her.

Harry
Ginny, has he been injured? I need to know he's safe . . .

Ginny
He insisted. He was the only one small enough to crawl through the grate. I tried to stop him.

Harry
Just tell me he's okay.

Act Four Scene Eleven

Albus

I'm fine, Dad. I promise.

Harry keeps advancing towards Delphi.

Harry

A lot of people have tried to hurt me – but my son! You dare hurt my son!

Delphi

I only wanted to know my father.

These words take Harry by surprise.

Harry

You can't remake your life. You'll always be an orphan. That never leaves you.

Delphi

Just let me – see him.

Harry

I can't and I won't.

Delphi **(truly pitiful)**

Then kill me.

Harry thinks a moment.

Harry
I can't do that either . . .

Albus
What? Dad? She's dangerous.

Harry
No, Albus . . .

Albus
But she's a murderer – I've seen her murder—

Harry turns and looks at his son and then at Ginny.

Harry
Yes. Albus, she's a murderer, and we're not.

Hermione
We have to be better than them.

Ron
Yeah, it's annoying but it's what we learnt.

Act Four Scene Eleven

Delphi
Take my mind. Take my memory.
Make me forget who I am.

Ron
No. We'll take you back to our time.

Hermione
And you'll go to Azkaban. Same as
your mother.

Draco
Where you'll rot.

**Harry hears a noise. A hissing
noise.**

**And then there is a noise like
death – a noise like nothing else
we've heard before.**

Haaarry Pottttter . . .

Scorpius
What's that?

Harry
No. No. Not yet.

Albus
  What?

Ron
  Voldemort.

Delphi
  Father?

Hermione
  Now? Here?

Delphi
  Father!

Draco
  Silencio! **(Delphi is gagged.)**
Wingardium Leviosa! **(She is sent
upwards and away.)**

Harry
  He's coming. He's coming right now.

**Voldemort comes through the
back of stage, and across it, and
walks down into the auditorium. He
brings death with him. And everyone
knows it.**

Act Four
Scene Twelve

Godric's Hollow, 1981

**Harry looks after
Voldemort helplessly.**

Harry
   Voldemort is going to kill my mum
and dad, and there's nothing I can do to
stop him.

Draco
   That's not true.

Scorpius
   Dad, now is not the time . . .

Albus
   There is something you could do – to
stop him. But you won't.

507

Draco
That's heroic.

Ginny takes Harry's hand.

Ginny
You don't have to watch, Harry. We can go home.

Harry
I'm letting it happen . . . of course I have to watch.

Hermione
Then we'll all witness it.

Ron
We'll all watch.

We hear unfamiliar voices . . .

James **(from off)**
Lily, take Harry and go! It's him! Go! Run! I'll hold him off . . .

There is a blast, and then a laugh.

You keep away, you understand – you keep away.

Voldemort **(from off)**
Avada Kedavra!

**Harry flinches as green light
flashes around the auditorium.**

**Albus takes his hand. Harry
grasps hold of it. He needs it.**

Albus
He did everything he could.

**Ginny rises beside Harry,
and takes his other hand. He leans
into them, they're holding him up
now.**

Harry
That's my mum, at the window.
I can see my mother, she looks
beautiful.

**There's the sound of banging as
doors are blasted off.**

Lily **(from off)**
Not Harry, not Harry, please not
Harry . . .

Voldemort **(from off)**
Stand aside, you silly girl . . . stand aside now . . .

Lily **(from off)**
Not Harry, please no, take me, kill me instead . . .

Voldemort **(from off)**
This is my last warning—

Lily **(from off)**
Not Harry! Please . . . have mercy . . . have mercy . . . not my son! Please – I'll do anything.

Voldemort **(from off)**
Avada Kedavra!

And it's like lightning passes through Harry's body. He's sent to the floor, a pure mess of grief.

And a noise like a shrunken scream descends and ascends around us.

And we just watch.

Act Four Scene Twelve

And slowly what was there is no longer there.

And the stage transforms and rotates.

And Harry and his family and his friends are rotated off and away.

———

Act Four

Scene Thirteen

Godric's Hollow, Inside James and Lily Potter's House, 1981

**And we're in the ruins of a house.
A house that has undergone
a vicious attack.**

Hagrid walks through the ruins.

Hagrid
James?

He looks about himself.

Lily??

**He walks slowly, unwilling to see
too much too soon. He is entirely
overwhelmed.**

512

And then he sees them, and he stops, and he says nothing.

Oh. Oh. That's not – that's not – I weren't . . . they told me, but – I were hoping for better . . .

He looks at them and bows his head. He mutters a few words and then takes some crumpled flowers from his deep pockets and lays them on the floor.

I'm sorry, they told me, he told me, Dumbledore told me, I can't wait with yeh. Them Muggles are coming yeh see with their flashing blues and they won't 'preciate a big lummox like me would they?

He lets out a sob.

Hard though it is to leave yeh. I want yeh to know – yeh won't be forgotten – not by me – not by anyfolk.

And then he hears a sound – the sound of a baby snuffling. Hagrid

turns towards it, walking with more
intensity now.

He looks down and stands over the
crib, which seems to radiate light.

Well. Hello. Yeh must be Harry. Hello,
Harry Potter. I'm Rubeus Hagrid. And I'm
gonna be yer friend whether yeh like it
or not. 'Cos yeh've had it tough, not
that yeh know it yet. An' yer gonna
need friends. Now yeh best come with
me don't yeh think?

As flashing blue lights fill the room
giving it an almost ethereal glow, he
lifts Harry gently into his arms.

And then – without looking back –
he strides away through the house.

And we descend into soft black.

—⁓—

Act Four

Scene Fourteen

Hogwarts, Classroom

Scorpius and Albus run into a room, full of excitement. They slam the door after themselves.

Scorpius
   I can't quite believe I did that.

Albus
   I can't quite believe you did that either.

Scorpius
   Rose Granger-Weasley. I asked out Rose Granger-Weasley.

Albus
   And she said no.

Scorpius

But I asked her. I planted the acorn. The acorn that will grow into our eventual marriage.

Albus

You are aware that you're an utter fantasist.

Scorpius

And I'd agree with you – only Polly Chapman did ask me to the School Ball . . .

Albus

In an alternate reality where you were significantly – really significantly, more popular – a different girl asked you out – and that means—

Scorpius

And yes, logic would dictate I should be pursuing Polly – or allowing her to pursue me – she's a notorious beauty after all – but a Rose is a Rose.

Albus

You know logic would dictate that you're a freak? Rose hates you.

Scorpius
Correction, she used to hate me, but did you see the look in her eyes when I asked? That wasn't hate, that was pity.

Albus
And pity's good?

Scorpius
Pity is a start my friend, a foundation on which to build a palace – a palace of love.

Albus
I honestly thought I'd be the first of us to get a girlfriend.

Scorpius
Oh, you will, undoubtedly, probably that new smoky-eyed Potions professor – she's old enough for you, right?

Albus
I don't have a thing about older women!

Scorpius
And you've got time – a lot of time –

to seduce her. Because Rose is going to take years to persuade.

Albus
I admire your confidence.

Rose comes past them on the stairs, she looks at them both.

Rose
Hi.

Neither boy knows quite how to reply – she looks at Scorpius.

Rose
This is only going to be weird if you let it be weird.

Scorpius
Received and entirely understood.

Rose
Okay. 'Scorpion King'.

She walks off with a smile on her face. Scorpius and Albus look at each other. Albus grins and punches Scorpius on the arm.

Act Four Scene Fourteen

Albus
Maybe you're right – pity is a start.

Scorpius
Are you heading to Quidditch?
Slytherin are playing Hufflepuff – it's a
big one—

Albus
I thought we hated Quidditch?

Scorpius
People can change. Besides, I've been
practising. I think I might make the
team eventually. Come on.

Albus
I can't. My dad's arranged to come
up—

Scorpius
He's taking time away from the
Ministry?

Albus
He wants to go on a walk –
something to show me – share with me
– something.

Scorpius
A walk?

Albus
I know, I think it's a bonding thing or something similarly vomit-inducing. Still, you know, I think I'll go.

Scorpius reaches in and hugs Albus.

What's this? I thought we decided we don't hug.

Scorpius
I wasn't sure. Whether we should. In this new version of us I had in my head.

Albus
Better ask Rose if it's the right thing to do.

Scorpius
Ha! Yeah. Right.

The two boys dislocate and grin at each other.

Act Four Scene Fourteen

Albus
    I'll see you at dinner.

———

Act Four
Scene Fifteen

A Beautiful Hill

**Harry and Albus walk up a hill on
a beautiful summer's day.**

**They say nothing, enjoying the sun
on their faces as they climb.**

Harry
    So are you ready?

Albus
    For what?

Harry
    Well, there's the fourth-year exams –
and then the fifth year – big year – in
my fifth year I did—

Act Four   Scene Fifteen

He looks at Albus. He smiles. He talks quickly.

I did a lot of stuff. Some of it good. Some of it bad. A lot of it quite confusing.

Albus
   Good to know.

Harry smiles.

I got to watch them – you know – for a bit – your mum and dad. They were – you had fun together. Your dad used to love to do this smoke ring thing with you where you . . . well, you couldn't stop giggling.

Harry
   Yes?

Albus
   I think you'd have liked them. And I think me, Lily and James would have liked them too.

Harry nods. There's a slightly uncomfortable silence. Both are trying

to reach each other here, both are failing.

Harry
    You know, I thought I'd lost him – Voldemort – I thought I'd lost him – and then my scar started hurting again and I had dreams of him and I could even speak Parseltongue again and I started to feel like I'd not changed at all – that he'd never let me go –

Albus
    And had he?

Harry
    The part of me that was Voldemort died a long time ago, but it wasn't enough to be physically rid of him – I had to be mentally rid of him. And that – is a lot to learn for a forty-year-old man.

He looks at Albus.

    That thing I said to you – it was unforgiveable, and I can't ask you to forget it but I can hope we move past it.

Act Four Scene Fifteen

I'm going to try to be a better dad for you, Albus. I am going to try and – be honest with you and . . .

Albus
Dad, you don't need to—

Harry
You told me you don't think I'm scared of anything, and that – I mean, I'm scared of everything. I mean, I'm afraid of the dark, did you know that?

Albus
Harry Potter is afraid of the dark?

Harry
I don't like small spaces and – I've never told anyone this but I don't much like – **(he hesitates before saying this)** pigeons.

Albus
You don't like pigeons?

Harry (he scrunches up his face)
Nasty, pecky, dirty things. They give me the creeps.

Part Two

Albus
But pigeons are harmless!

Harry
I know. But the thing that scares me most, Albus Severus Potter, is being a dad to you. Because I'm operating without wires here. Most people at least have a dad to base themselves on – and either try to be or try not to be. I've got nothing – or very little. So I'm learning, okay? And I'm going to try with everything I've got – to be a good dad for you.

Albus
And I'll try and be a better son. I know I'm not James, Dad, I'll never be like you two—

Harry
James is nothing like me.

Albus
Isn't he?

Harry
Everything comes easy for James. My childhood was a constant struggle.

Act Four Scene Fifteen

Albus
So was mine. So you're saying – am I – like you?

Harry smiles at Albus.

Harry
Actually you're more like your mum – bold, fierce, funny – which I like – which I think makes you a pretty great son.

Albus
I almost destroyed the world.

Harry
Delphi wasn't going anywhere, Albus – you brought her out into the light and you found a way for us to fight her. You may not see it now, but you saved us.

Albus
But shouldn't I have done better?

Harry
You don't think I ask myself the same questions?

Albus (stomach sinking further, he knows this is not what his dad would do)

And then – when we caught her – I wanted to kill her.

Harry

You'd watched her murder Craig, you were angry Albus, and that's okay. And you wouldn't have done it.

Albus

How do you know that? Maybe that's my Slytherin side. Maybe that's what the Sorting Hat saw in me.

Harry

I don't understand your head, Albus – actually, you know what, you're a teenager, I shouldn't be able to under-stand your head, but I do understand your heart. I didn't – for a long time – but thanks to this – 'escapade' – I know what you got in there. Slytherin, Gryffindor, whatever label you've been given – I know – know – that heart is a good one – yeah, whether you like it or not, you're on your way to being some wizard.

Act Four Scene Fifteen

Albus
Oh, I'm not going to be a wizard, I'm going into pigeon racing. I'm quite excited about it.

Harry grins.

Harry
Those names you have – they shouldn't be a burden. Albus Dumbledore had his trials too you know – and Severus Snape, well, you know all about him—

Albus
They were good men.

Harry
They were great men, with huge flaws, and you know what – those flaws almost made them greater.

Albus looks around himself.

Albus
Dad? Why are we here?

Harry
This is where I often come.

Part Two

Albus
> But this is a graveyard . . .

Harry
> And here is Cedric's grave . . .

Albus
> Dad?

Harry
> The boy who was killed – Craig Bowker – how well did you know him?

Albus
> Not well enough.

Harry
> I didn't know Cedric well enough either. He could have played Quidditch for England. Or been a brilliant Auror. He could have been anything. And Amos is right – he was stolen. So I come here. Just to say sorry. When I can.

Albus
> That's a – good thing to do.

Albus joins his dad in front of Cedric's grave. Harry smiles at his son and looks up at the sky.

Harry
   I think it's going to be a nice day.

He touches his son's shoulder. And the two of them – just slightly – melt together.

Albus **(smiles)**
   So do I.

───

The End

Glossary

Character Names

Albus Dumbledore: al-bus dum-bull-dor
Hogwarts Headmaster, founder of the Order of the Phoenix, with a fondness for sherbet lemons and knitting patterns.

Albus Potter: al-bus pot-ter
Middle child of Harry Potter and Ginny Weasley.

Amos Diggory: ay-moss dig-gor-ree
Father of the late Cedric Diggory who worked for the Department of the Regulation and Control of Magical Creatures.

Astoria Malfoy: ass-stor-ree-ah mal-foy
Draco's wife and caring mother of Scorpius.

Aunt Petunia: **ah-nt pe-chu-nee-a**

Dudley's devoted mother, Lily's Muggle sister and Vernon Dursley's wife.

Bane: **bay-n**

Bane is a centaur who lives in the Forbidden Forest at Hogwarts. A man to the waist with the body of a horse, he is black-haired and wild-looking.

Bellatrix Lestrange: **bel-luh-triks luh-stray-nj**

One of Voldemort's most loyal Death Eaters. A dangerous witch and skilled dueller, she was killed by Molly Weasley during the Battle of Hogwarts.

Cedric Diggory: **sed-rik dig-gor-ree**

Popular Hufflepuff Seeker and competitor in the Triwizard Tournament. Murdered by Peter Pettigrew at Voldemort's command.

Delphi Diggory: **del-fee dig-gor-ree**

A young caregiver at St Oswald's Home for Old Witches and Wizards.

Character Names

Dolores Umbridge: **duh-law-rez um-brij**

Ministry bureaucrat and one-time Hogwarts professor. She was eventually sent to Azkaban from crimes against Muggle-borns.

Draco Malfoy: **dray-ko mal-foy**

Pure-blood wizard, proud Slytherin and Harry Potter's arch rival at Hogwarts. Later, father to Scorpius Malfoy.

Dudley Dursley: **dud-lee durs-lee**

Harry Potter's cousin. The spoiled son of Vernon and Petunia Dursley.

Ginny Potter: **jin-nee pot-ter**

The youngest Weasley child. Brave, tenacious and an accomplished Quidditch player, Ginny went on to marry Harry Potter. Mother to James, Albus and Lily Potter.

Hagrid: **hag-rid**

The half-giant Hogwarts gamekeeper. Tirelessly loyal friend to both Harry and Dumbledore.

Glossary

Harry Potter: har-ree pot-ter
  The Boy Who Lived. Singled out by Lord Voldemort at birth to be his greatest rival, and our hero. Married to Ginny Weasley, father to James, Albus and Lily Potter.

Hermione Granger:
her-my-oh-nee grayn-jer
  From bookish Muggle-born to one of Gryffindor's bravest, she went on to marry childhood friend Ron Weasley. Mother to Rose and Hugo Weasley.

James Potter: jay-mz pot-ter
  Gryffindor student and eldest son of Harry Potter and Ginny Weasley.

Lily Potter (daughter):
lil-lee pot-ter
  Harry and Ginny's youngest child, named after Harry's late mother.

Lily Potter (mother): lil-lee
pot-ter
  Harry's mother. A talented Muggle-born witch who was murdered by Voldemort during the First Wizarding War.

Character Names

Lord Voldemort: law-d vole-duh-mor

Formerly known as Tom Marvolo Riddle and commonly referred to as He-Who-Must-Not-Be-Named. The most powerful Dark wizard of all time until his demise at the hands of Harry Potter.

Madam Hooch: mad-um hooch

Madam Hooch was a witch and the flying instructor at Hogwarts School of Witchcraft and Wizardry.

Moaning Myrtle: mow-ning mur-tul

The sullen ghost of Hogwarts student Myrtle Warren, killed by Salazar Slytherin's Basillisk at Voldemort's command. She dwells in the girls' bathroom on the first floor of the school.

Professor McGonagall: pro-fess-or mak-gon-a-gul

The strict but fair Head of Gryffindor house, Transfiguration teacher and Headmistress at Hogwarts, who is of great help to Harry.

Rodolphus Lestrange:
rud–dol–fus luh–stray–nj

Rodolphus Lestrange was a pure-blood wizard and Death Eater, brother of Rabastan and husband to Bellatrix Lestrange.

Ron Weasley: **ron wee–z–lee**

One of Harry Potter's two best friends, fellow Gryffindor, and youngest Weasley son. Married Hermione Granger, father of Rose and Hugo.

Rose Granger–Weasley: **rows grayn–jer wee–z–lee**

Daughter of Hermione Granger and Ron Weasley.

Scorpius Malfoy: **skor–pee–us mal–foy**

Draco and Astoria Malfoy's son.

Severus Snape: **sev–ur–us snay–p**

Hogwarts Potions master, Head of Slytherin house and former Death Eater. Held a grudge against Harry throughout his time at school, and was secretly in love with Harry's mother Lily. Snape died at the Battle of Hogwarts.

Sorting hat: **sor-ting hat**
Enchanted hat that once belonged to Godric Gryffindor and sorts students into Hogwarts houses.

Trolley Witch: **trol-ee wich**
Witch who operates the Hogwarts Express food trolley on the journey to and from Hogwarts School of Witchcraft and Wizardry.

Uncle Vernon: **un-kul vur-nun**
Harry Potter's uncle by marriage, Petunia's husband and Dudley's father. Expresses his prejudiced views at every opportunity.

Viktor Krum: **vik-tor krum**
Viktor Krum is an international Quidditch player and Seeker from Bulgaria, and is a student at the Durmstrang Institute.

Wizarding Words

Alohomora: al–oh–ha–mor–ah
A charm that unlocks and opens doors and windows.

Aurors: or–rurs
Ministry of Magic employees in charge of investigating crimes related to Dark magic.

Avada Kedavra: uh–vaar–dah kuh–daar–vrah
Powerful curse which instantly kills the victim. One of the three Unforgivable Curses.

Azkaban: az–kuh–ban
An island prison in the middle of the North Sea. Home to dangerous wizards and witches.

Glossary

Bathilda Bagshot: bah-thil-duh bag-shot
Professor Bathilda Bagshot was a noted historian and the author of
A History of Magic among other books.

Beauxbatons: boh-bat-tunz
The Beauxbatons Academy of Magic, thought to be situated somewhere in the Pyrenees. Beauxbatons has a preponderance for French students, though Spanish, Portuguese, Dutch, Luxembourgians and Belgians also attend.

Boomslang: boom-slang
A small, magical snake.

Brachiabindo: brak-kee-ah-bin-doh
A spell used to bind an opponent.

Centaur: sen-tor
Half-man, half-horse, centaurs are highly intelligent and possibly clairvoyant. They often dwell in the Forbidden Forest.

Wizarding Words

Confringo: cun-fring-go
A spell that causes anything that it comes into contact with to explode.

Confundus: cun-fund-us
A charm which bewitches a person into altering their behaviour.

Crucio: kroo-shee-yoh
One of the three Unforgivable Curses, the Cruciatus Curse causes agonising pain.

Dementor: duh-men-tor
The guards of Azkaban, they feed on human happiness and can extract souls with their Dementor's Kiss.

Divination: div-in-nay-shun
A branch of magic dedicated to fore-seeing the future.

Durmstrang: derm-strang
The Durmstrang Institute is a wizarding school, believed to be situated in the far north of Europe.

Engorgement: en-gorj-ment
A charm that causes the target to swell.

Glossary

Engorgio: en-gorj-ee-oh
The incantation that is spoken to produce the Engorgement charm.

Expecto Patronum: ex-pek-toh pat-tro-num
Wizards can use this charm to summon an animal guardian to defend them from Dementors and other Dark creatures.

Expelliarmus: ex-spel-lee-ar-mus
A handy, even life-saving spell for removing an object from an enemy's grasp.

Expulso: ex-pul-so
A spell used to produce immense explosions.

Firewhisky: fie-yah-wisk-kee
An alcoholic drink consumed by wizards and witches.

Flipendo: flip-pen-doh
A jinx to physically repel an object or person.

Wizarding Words

Fulgari: ful-gar-ree
A spell used to bind an opponent's arms in vicious, luminous cords.

Gillyweed: gil-lee-weed
A magical plant that allows a person to breathe underwater.

Gobstones: gob-stow-nz
An ancient wizarding game that resembles marbles. Every time a point is conceded, the winning stone squirts a foul-smelling liquid into the loser's face.

Graphorns: graf-forns
A large and greyish purple beast with a humped back and two very long, sharp horns. Possess an extremely aggressive nature.

Gringotts: grin-gots
A wizarding bank, run by goblins.

Gryffindor: grif-in-dor
The Hogwarts house that values courage, bravery and determination. Gryffindor's crest is a lion and its colours are red and gold.

Glossary

Hogsmeade: hogz-mee-d
   An entirely wizarding village in Britain. Home of the Three Broomsticks and Hog's Head pubs.

Honeydukes: hun-nee-dyooks
   A famous wizarding sweet shop located in Hogsmeade.

Hufflepuff: huf-ful-puff
   The Hogwarts house that welcomes kindness, loyalty and patience. Hufflepuff's crest is a badger and its colours are yellow and black.

Imperius: im-peer-ree-us
   One of the three Unforgiveable Curses, it allows the caster to control another person's actions.

Magick Moste Evile: maj-jik mow-st ee-vul
   A book which covers dark magic.

Merpeople: mur-pee-pul
   Underwater beasts who have a rocky relationship with the wizarding world.

Wizarding Words

Mobilicorpus:
moh-bil-lee-cor-puss
A spell used to physically move the body of someone.

Mudblood: mud-blud
A highly derogatory term for a Muggle-born wizard or witch.

Muggle: mug-gul
Non-magical people, most of whom are completely unaware of the existence of the wizarding world. The term is usually applied affectionately.

Obscuro: ob-skiyu-ro
A spell used to conjure a blindfold over the eyes of a victim.

Owled: a-wuld
To receive a postal delivery of either a letter or parcel, by owl post.

Owlery: a-wol-er-ree
A place in Hogwarts where owls reside during the school year.

Glossary

Parseltongue: par-sul-tung
The rare ability to speak the language of snakes.

Patronus: pat-troh-nuss
A magical protector that takes the form of an animal based on a Wizard's personal traits. It is conjured to defend the Wizard from threats, such as Dementors.

Polyjuice: pol-lee joos
A potion that allows the drinker to transform into another person for a limited amount of time.

Portkey: port-kee
An inanimate object enchanted to transport anyone who touches it to a specific destination.

Quidditch: kwid-dich
A magical sport played on broomsticks. The game ends when a player called the Seeker catches the Snitch – a magical, winged, golden ball.

Wizarding Words

Ravenclaw: ray-vun-clor
The Hogwarts house that champions wisdom, wit and learning. Ravenclaw's crest is an eagle, and its colours are blue and bronze.

Rictusempra: rik-tus-sem-pra
A tickling charm.

Silencio: sil-len-see-oh
A charm that renders the victim temporarily mute, working on both beasts and beings.

Slytherin: sli-th-ur-in
The Hogwarts house that favours ambition and cunning. It has a reputation for producing Dark wizards. Slytherin's crest is a serpent and its colours are green and silver.

Specialis Revelio:
spesh-sha-lis ruh-vel-ee-oh
The incantation of a spell that allows the caster to reveal any charms or hexes.

Squib: skw-ib
An individual born into a wizarding family but has no magical abilities.

Glossary

Stupefy: stoo-pih-fi
The Stunning Spell.

Thestrals: thess-truls
A rare breed of winged horse which possess the power of invisibility. Considered unlucky by many wizards, they are only visible to those who have seen death.

Transfigure: tranz-fig-ur
A complex magic used to alter the form of an object.

Triwizard tournament: try-wiz-urd tor-nuh-ment
A legendary tournament that pits champions from three wizarding schools against each other in a competition of magical prowess.

Upper Flagley: up-pur flag-lee
The location of St Oswald's Home for Old Witches and Wizards, a wizarding nursing home for the elderly.

Wizarding Words

Whomping Willow: **womp-ping wil-loh**
A violent tree which stands alone in the Hogwarts grounds.

Wingardium Leviosa:
win-gaar-dee-um lev-ee-oh-saar
A simple charm that is used for making objects float or fly.

Harry Potter and the Cursed Child Parts One and Two was first produced by Sonia Friedman Productions, Colin Callender and Harry Potter Theatrical Productions. It premiered at the Palace Theatre, London, on 30 July 2016 with the following cast.

Cast names in alphabetical order

Craig Bowker Jr	Jeremy Ang Jones
Moaning Myrtle, Lily Potter Sr	Annabel Baldwin
Uncle Vernon, Severus Snape, Lord Voldemort	Paul Bentall
Scorpius Malfoy	Anthony Boyle
Albus Potter	Sam Clemmett
Hermione Granger	Noma Dumezweni
Polly Chapman	Claudia Grant

Cast Names

Hagrid, Sorting Hat	Chris Jarman
Yann Fredericks	James Le Lacheur
Aunt Petunia, Madam Hooch, Dolores Umbridge	Helena Lymbery
Amos Diggory, Albus Dumbledore	Barry McCarthy
Trolley Witch, Professor Mcgonagall	Sandy McDade
Station Master	Adam McNamara
Ginny Potter	Poppy Miller
Cedric Diggory, James Potter Jr, James Potter Sr	Tom Milligan
Dudley Dursley, Karl Jenkins, Viktor Krum	Jack North
Harry Potter	Jamie Parker

Cast Names

Draco Malfoy	Alex Price
Bane	Nuno Silva
Rose Granger-Weasley, Young Hermione	Cherrelle Skeete
Delphi Diggory	Esther Smith
Ron Weasley	Paul Thornley
Young Harry Potter	Rudi Goodman
	Alfred Jones
	Bili Keogh
	Ewan Rutherford
	Nathaniel Smith
	Dylan Standen
Lily Potter Jr	Zoe Brough
	Cristina Fray
	Christiana Hutchings

Cast Names

Other roles played by

Nicola Alexis, Jeremy Ang Jones, Rosemary Annabella, Annabel Baldwin, Jack Bennett, Paul Bentall, Morag Cross, Claudia Grant, James Howard, Lowri James, Chris Jarman, Martin Johnston, James Le Lacheur, Helena Lymbery, Barry McCarthy, Andrew McDonald, Adam McNamara, Tom Milligan, Jack North, Stuart Ramsay, Nuno Silva, Cherrelle Skeete

Swings

Helen Aluko, Morag Cross, Chipo Kureya, Tom Mackley, Joshua Wyatt

Nuno Silva	Movement Captain
Jack North	Assistant Movement Captain
Morag Cross	Voice Captain

Creative and Production Team

Original Story	J.K. Rowling, John Tiffany, Jack Thorne
Playwright	Jack Thorne
Director	John Tiffany
Movement Director	Steven Hoggett
Set Designer	Christine Jones
Costume Designer	Katrina Lindsay
Composer & Arranger	Imogen Heap
Lighting Designer	Neil Austin
Sound Designer	Gareth Fry
Illusions & Magic	Jamie Harrison

Music Supervisor & Arranger	Martin Lowe
Casting Director	Julia Horan CDG

Production Manager	Gary Beestone
Production Stage Manager	Sam Hunter
Associate Director	Des Kennedy
Associate Movement Director	Neil Bettles
Associate Set Designer	Brett J. Banakis
Associate Sound Designer	Pete Malkin
Illusions & Magic Associate	Chris Fisher
Casting Associate	Lotte Hines

Creative and Production Team

Assistant Lighting Designer	Adam King
Costume Design Supervisor	Sabine Lemaître
Hair, Wigs & Make-Up	Carole Hancock
Props Supervisors	Lisa Buckley, Mary Halliday
Music Editor	Phij Adams
Music Production	Imogen Heap
Special Effects	Jeremy Chernick
Video Design	Finn Ross, Ash Woodward
Dialect Coach	Daniele Lydon
Voice Coach	Richard Ryder
Company Stage Manager	Richard Clayton
Stage Manager	Jordan Noble-Davies
Deputy Stage Manager	Jenefer Tait

Creative and Production Team

Assistant Stage Managers	Oliver Bagwell Purefoy, Tom Gilding, Sally Inch, Ben Sherratt
Resident Director	Pip Minnithorpe
Head Of Wardrobe	Amy Gillot
Deputy Head Of Wardrobe	Laura Watkins
Wardrobe Assistants	Kate Anderson, Leanne Hired
Dressers	George Amielle, Melissa Cooke, Rosie Etheridge, John Ovenden, Emilee Swift
Head Of Hair, Wigs & Make-Up	Nina Van Houten
Deputy Head Of Hair, Wigs & Make-Up	Alice Townes
Hair, Wigs & Make-Up Assistants	Charlotte Briscoe, Jacob Fessey, Cassie Murphie
Head Of Sound	Chris Reid

Creative and Production Team

Deputy Head Of Sound	Rowena Edwards
Sound No. 3	Laura Caplin
Sfx Operator	Callum Donaldson
Head Of Automation	Josh Peters
Deputy Head Of Automation	Jamie Lawrence
Automation No. 3	Jamie Robson
Show Chief Lx	David Treanor
Performer Flying Technician	Paul Gurney
Chaperones	David Russell, Eleanor Dowling

General Management	Sonia Friedman Productions
Executive Director	Diane Benjamin
Executive Producer	Pam Skinner
Associate Producer	Fiona Stewart

Creative and Production Team

Assistant Producer	Ben Canning
General Management Assistant	Max Bittleston
Production Assistant	Imogen Clare-Wood
Marketing Manager	Laura Jane Elliott
Revenue Manager	Mark Payn
Associate Producer (Development)	Lucie Lovatt
Development Assistant	Lydia Rynne
Literary Associate	Jack Bradley
Office Assistant	Jordan Eaton
House Seats Assistant	Vicky Ngoma

Biographies of the Original Story Team

J.K. ROWLING
Original story

J.K. Rowling is the author of the seven Harry Potter novels, which have sold over 450 million copies and have been translated into 79 languages, and three companion books originally published for charity. She is also the author of **The Casual Vacancy**, a novel for adults published in 2012, and, under the pseudonym of Robert Galbraith, is the author of the Cormoran Strike crime series. J.K. Rowling is making her screenwriting debut and is a producer on the film **Fantastic Beasts and Where to Find Them**, a further extension of the Wizarding World, due for release in November 2016.

JOHN TIFFANY
Original story and director

John Tiffany directed **Once**, for which he was the recipient of multiple awards both in the West End and on Broadway. As Associate Director of the Royal Court, his work includes **The Twits**, **Hope** and **The Pass**. He was the director of **Let the Right One In** for the National Theatre of Scotland, which transferred to the Royal Court, West End and St Ann's Warehouse. His other work for the National Theatre of Scotland includes **Macbeth** (also Broadway), **Enquirer**, **The Missing**, **Peter Pan**, **The House of Bernarda Alba**, **Transform Caithness: Hunter**, **Be Near Me**, **Nobody Will Ever Forgive Us**, **The Bacchae**, **Black Watch**, for which he won the Olivier and Critics' Circle Best Director Awards, **Elizabeth Gordon Quinn** and **Home: Glasgow**. Other recent credits include **The Glass Menagerie** at ART and on Broadway and **The Ambassador** at BAM. Tiffany was Associate Director of the National Theatre of Scotland from 2005 to 2012, and was a Radcliffe Fellow at Harvard University in the 2010–2011 academic year.

Story Team Biographies

JACK THORNE
Original story and playwright

Jack Thorne writes for theatre, film, television and radio. His theatre credits include **Hope** and **Let the Right One In**, both directed by John Tiffany, **The Solid Life of Sugar Water** for the Graeae Theatre Company and the National Theatre, **Bunny** for the Edinburgh Fringe Festival, **Stacy** for the Trafalgar Studios, and **2nd May 1997** and **When You Cure Me** for the Bush. His adaptations include **The Physicists** for the Donmar Warehouse and **Stuart: A Life Backwards** for HighTide. On film his credits include **War Book, A Long Way Down** and **The Scouting Book for Boys**. For television his credits include **The Last Panthers, Don't Take My Baby, This Is England, The Fades, Glue, Cast-Offs** and **National Treasure**. He won BAFTAs in 2016 for Best Mini-Series (**This Is England '90**) and Best Single Drama (**Don't Take My Baby**), and in 2012 for Best Drama Series (**The Fades**) and Best Mini-Series (**This Is England '88**).

Acknowledgements

All the actors from the Cursed Child workshops, Mel Kenyon, Rachel Taylor, Alexandria Horton, Imogen Clare-Wood, Florence Rees, Jenefer Tait, David Nock, Rachel Mason, Colin, Neil, Sonia, everyone at SFP and The Blair Partnership, Rebecca Salt from JKR PR, Nica Burns and all the staff at the Palace Theatre, and, of course, our incredible cast who helped shape every word.